COSMOLOGY AND CHRISTIANITY

IS VOLUME

127

OF THE

Twentieth Century Encyclopedia of Catholicism

UNDER SECTION

XIII

CATHOLICISM AND SCIENCE

IT IS ALSO THE

132ND

VOLUME IN ORDER OF PUBLICATION

Edited by HENRI DANIEL-ROPS of the Académie Française

COSMOLOGY
AND CHRISTIANITY

By J. V. PEACH

HAWTHORN BOOKS · PUBLISHERS · *New York*

First Edition, August, 1965

NIHIL OBSTAT

Joannes M. T. Barton, S.T.D., L.S.S.

Censor Deputatus

IMPRIMATUR

Patritius Casey

Vicarius Generalis

Westmonasterii, die 28 JUNII MCMLXV

H-9569

CONTENTS

INTRODUCTION

"Two things fill the mind with ever new and increasing admiration and awe, the more often and the more steadily we reflect on them: the starry heavens above and the moral law within" (Kant, *Critique of Practical Reason*).

When Kant wrote the above he was expressing a seemingly universal emotion; and while thinking on morals has lost none of its fascination, neither have speculations on the nature of the heavens. Furthermore, these speculations have proved to be of considerable interest even outside professional scientific circles. The continued popular interest in astronomy is witnessed by the success of the numerous elementary treatments of astronomical questions that have been published in recent years, and by the popularity of quite technical broadcast discussions of lunar, solar and stellar problems. But by far the most interesting feature of modern astronomical work from the point of view of the layman seems to be cosmology, the study of the universe in its most large-scale aspects, the investigation of the origin, structure and evolution of the universe as a whole.

The former popularizers of the early advances in cosmology were Sir Arthur Eddington and Sir James Jeans, whose books achieved a considerable success in stimulating general interest in the remarkable developments which stemmed from observations obtained by the large telescopes in the United States. Eddington had himself been closely associated with the earlier applications of the General Theory of Relativity to cosmology, and possessed a keen interest in philosophy which led him to speculate widely on the relevance of this new science to the traditional ideas of order and unity in the universe, and then to the question of creation. This progress from consideration of the physical properties of the universe to consideration of more ultimate questions is quite natural. While scientific work in other fields can also prompt metaphysical questionings, cosmology, by the very fact that it takes the nature of the totality of material things as its subject matter, obviously leads to some philosophical questions more directly. This has also been clearly brought out more recently in expositions of modern work by Professors Lovell and Hoyle, who both discuss conclusions from cosmological theories as to man's status in the universe, and so on.

Obviously, this tendency to argue from theories of the structure of the universe to conclusions about, for instance, the possibility or the manner of creation is in no way confined to recent years. Although it is only in this century that we can be said to have established truly scientific cosmologies, the more or less naïve views of former times had the most profound effects on thinking in philosophy and theology. Pre-Renaissance astronomy was not a mere specialist branch of natural science, but a means of investigating a world-picture that would be intimately interwoven with one's whole understanding of life. Indeed, so intimately were ultimate concepts intermingled with a theory of the universe that in some cases any change in the theory might necessitate a complete remoulding of religious and moral principles. It is this connection between ideas on the structure of the universe and other elements in a coherent view of reality that has given rise to many of the problems and confusions with which this book is concerned.

Illustrations of this can easily be given. It is well known that Aristotle developed a philosophical system with a high degree of internal consistency, from which he deduced the phenomena of the motions of the planets and the fixed stars. He deduced that the earth is at the centre of the universe and at perfect rest, that the universe itself is spherical and of finite extent, that the motions of the planets are long concentric circles and that the stars themselves are perfect spheres. When these ideas were advanced they were reasonably closely in agreement with observation, although there were even then observations that suggested some discrepancy. But quite clearly, when more refined observations disproved the Aristotelean theory point by point, the validity of the principles from which it was deduced, or the correctness of the deduction itself, is called in question. Today one would criticize both his basic theories of motion and of the four elements, and the soundness of his reasoning from these theories. But this serves to show that in a philosophical system in which a theory of the structure of the universe is closely linked with other elements in the system, a change in the physical picture of the universe can have repercussions in quite other fields than pure astronomy.

A further illustration can be drawn from the well-known controversy aroused by Galileo's championing of the Copernican heliocentric theory of the solar system. Those of his opponents who upheld the strict literal validity of the Scriptures maintained that the earth could not move round the sun, as Joshua had ordered the sun and not the earth to stand still. When it became generally accepted that the earth was in fact in motion, one had obviously to look with quite a new eye not only at the Book of Joshua, but also at other texts of considerably greater importance for both doctrine and morals.

Of particular interest today is the relation between the modern developments in cosmology and the traditional Christian view on the creation and conservation of the universe. Earlier world pictures had included accounts of creation which were either avowedly mythological, or claimed to be physically possible. They had offered suggestions as to the development of the world in terms of a struggle between opposing spiritual forces, or in terms of a transformation of matter according to its inherent properties. These accounts, although of a certain psychological or historical interest, are irrelevant to a correct understanding of the actual development of the universe. But modern astronomical research is now attempting to discover the precise course of this development, and although few facts are now securely established, one has the promise of a more and more exact account of the evolution of the universe. Not only has this scientific account offered a variety of physically possible modes of evolution, but speculations as to the origin of matter have been made which are of the greatest interest, as being on quite a different level from the speculations of the pre-scientific cosmologies. This remarkable advance in the possibility of exploring the nature of things not only possesses an intrinsic value as an exciting contribution to science, but is, perhaps, in some way relevant to a theological account of creation. Although it is highly doubtful whether this is in fact the case, it is of some importance to examine the exact nature of cosmology to see whether it is of any consequence for any other field of knowledge.

It is the aim of this book to sketch the observational and theoretical basis of cosmology so that an evaluation of its possible relevance to a Christian theology is feasible. Although my conclusion is that it is fundamentally irrelevant, it seems of value to give the reasons for this conclusion at length because of the remarkable confusion that surrounds this topic. Most of the perplexity that has been aroused by the use of the cosmological terms "the age of the universe" and "creation", for example, is due to a misunderstanding as to the precise nature of cosmological statements. It is a simple controversy indeed that can be settled by showing that a word is being used in more than one sense; but this is strangely true of some of the controversy that has arisen over the interrelations between cosmology and theology, and the reason that this kind of confusion has been so rife is that cosmology is a very difficult and highly technical subject. It is a subject that requires considerable knowledge of mathematical physics, and a keen critical sense with regard to the value of the observational evidence; and, further, it is a subject in which there are remarkably few well-established principles. It is clearly not possible to do such a branch of science justice in a brief account which is intended mainly for those with no technical knowledge of astronomy, but it is possible to give sufficient detail of the different cosmological theories to make clear, at the very least, what certain key cosmological statements do *not* mean.

This Introduction serves as a sketch of the background to the problems that have arisen in the relations between theology and cosmology. Suggestions as to the solution of these problems will wait until a fuller account has been given of the cosmological theories themselves.

THE DEVELOPMENT OF MODERN COSMOLOGY

The term cosmology has been applied to many branches of study with quite different objects and methods, from the speculations of some Pre-Socratic philosophers to the metaphysical view of nature of the Neo-Scholastics but, in its currently popular meaning, it is used to denote the modern science of the universe which can be said to have had its origin in Einstein's work on the General Theory of Relativity published in 1917. Einstein showed that a modification of the so-called field equations of General Relativity allowed a solution which appeared to represent the observable universe. This solution defined a model universe which, although finite in the spatial dimensions, was unbounded, and which had a uniform and static distribution of matter. As the astronomical observations of that time seemed to show a uniform large-scale distribution of matter and only small relative velocities for astronomical objects, this model universe was thought to provide a rough approximation to reality.

A further consideration of the field equations shortly afterwards by de Sitter showed that there was another solution for which objects would have the property of continually receding from one another. As this de Sitter model was, however, postulated to be void of matter, the recession property applying only to test-particles assumed to be of negligible mass, and as this continual recession had not been observed among astronomical objects, it was considered to be a solution of only mathematical interest. Further progress in the consideration of the implications of General Relativity with regard to the large-scale structure of the universe was made in the nineteen-twenties, chiefly by Friedmann, Weyl, Lemaître and Robertson, and theoretical model universes were discovered which were in accordance with relativity theory, and had a range of properties intermediate between the Einstein and the de Sitter models. Quite clearly, only one of the many possible models can be the "correct" one, if indeed these relativistic theories are actually capable of describing the world correctly.

It was only in 1929 that observational evidence became available which could lead to some form of choice among the theoretical models that had been discovered. Using the 100 in. Mount Wilson telescope Hubble found a relationship between the distances of the extragalactic nebulae and the red-shift of light in their spectra which, if the red-shift was interpreted in terms of the Doppler Effect, showed that the more distant these objects were, the more rapid was their velocity along the line-of-sight, and that this velocity was predominantly a velocity of recession. As this implies that the nebulae are receding from one another and that the matter of the observable universe is continually occupying a larger and larger volume, the model universe that Einstein first proposed, which had a static distribution of matter, was obviously excluded as a description of the universe. Attention switched to models which showed the matter in the universe to be expanding. Einstein and de Sitter published an investigation in 1932 of a model universe with finite density of matter and in which the space itself was regarded as expanding.

Model universes were also being constructed at this time which were not based directly on General Relativity. Milne developed the theory of Kinematic Relativity, and Milne and McCrea showed that model universes equivalent to those developed from General Relativity could be found on the basis of Newtonian mechanics in particular cases. Eddington was working on a highly a-prioristic theory emphasizing very strongly a connection between the physics of matter on the smallest scale (atomic physics, quantum physics) and the physics of matter on the largest scale (cosmology). This connection is also central to the cosmologies of Jordan and Dirac. Although these cosmologies have never been widely influential they are of some interest, as they stress what must surely be a final aim of scientific theory, that is, to provide a consistent and unified explanation of the behaviour of matter at all levels from fundamental particles to clusters of galaxies.

What was in some ways a radical break with the previous development of cosmological theory came after the War with the so-called Steady-State cosmologies. Although one of these theories, developed by Hoyle, is based on a modification of the field equations of General Relativity whereas the others are not, they all contain a novel element. This is the supposition that the universe as a whole is unchanging with time. But as the universe is observed to be expanding, a continuous creation of matter is postulated to keep the density of matter constant. Thus as distant galaxies recede from us until they are no longer visible, newly created matter condenses to form new galaxies so that their number in a given volume is unchanged in time. The suggestion that matter may be created is of course in contradiction to the generally accepted Principle of Conservation of Energy and Matter, but the rate of creation of matter needed to maintain a constant density throughout the universe can be shown to be too small to be detected in any conventional laboratory experiment. In these theories the universe is temporally unchanging and presents the same general aspects from any point apart from minor local irregularities. In the form in which the Steady-State theory is presented by Bondi and Gold this property of the model universe, that it presents the same approximate appearance no matter from where, or at what time, it is observed, is assumed as an initial postulate and the other properties of the model are deduced from this.

It might be remarked here that at the present time the theories appear to have run ahead of the observations, and further progress depends on carefully designed observations suited to test one or more predictions of the different models. But in its half-century of development cosmology has established itself as a branch of physical science that is destined to receive more and more attention. If not as firmly established as some other fields of astrophysics, it can no longer be dismissed, as was once common, as mere speculation.

THE NATURE OF MODERN COSMOLOGY

It is not at all clear that cosmology is a physical science as, for example, is nuclear physics. The problem of determining the properties of particular classes of objects in the universe, however difficult it may be technically, does not cause the perplexities both scientific and philosophical that surround the problem of determining the properties of the class containing all objects. So it is of interest in an account dealing with the relevance of cosmology to a study such as theology to gain a preliminary idea of the aims and limitations of this science.

Cosmology can be defined as the scientific study of the universe considered as a whole. Before this definition can be understood it must be made clear what the terms "scientific" and "universe" mean in this context. Cosmology cannot be scientific in the sense in which one calls the other physical sciences scientific, because of the uniqueness of its object. A science such as chemistry proceeds by the classical method of deducing laws from a number of instances, and by separating the factors governing a phenomenon by a series of experiments designed to test each factor separately. As cosmology has only one object, there being only one universe, this is not possible; furthermore, cosmology is an observational and not an experimental subject.

There are difficulties also in the definition of the object of this science, that is, the universe. Taking the definition given by the Concise Oxford Dictionary—"all existing things, the whole creation (and the Creator)"—obviously will not do, as there are many existent things that cosmology is not concerned with. The only possible definition is one with a direct physical significance, and the most suitable seems to be "the totality of observable events". Here "event" is used in the sense of relativity theory, meaning a point defined by three spatial co-ordinates and the time co-ordinate. This definition of the term "universe" would, however, exclude possible events which are beyond the range of our observations, that is, that are not physically connected to us in some way. Assuming the existence of such events, one can include them in another definition of the universe of the form, for example, of "the largest set of events that obey the laws of physics".

An interesting aspect of modern cosmological theories is that they all contain some elements of a cosmogony. This is inevitable, as they are all attempting to represent an obviously dynamic universe, and so must all contain a reference to the evolution of the system in the past and in the future. This will become clear in the discussion of the different theories later, when their widely differing aims and assumptions are considered. Perhaps then the reader will conclude that the only acceptable definition of cosmology is "what cosmologists do".

THE DEVELOPMENT OF CHRISTIAN VIEWS ON COSMOLOGY

The preoccupations of the theologian are not those of the natural scientist, and the theologian's interest in creation and his understanding of it is of quite a different order to that, say, of an astronomer. While an astronomer is concerned above all with the question of how the universe originated and developed, the theologian is interested rather in the relationship of God to the material universe in principle, than in the details of the physical laws that arise from this relationship. It is unfortunate, though perhaps inevitable, that many theologians have in the past tended to talk as though these details were within the competence of their subject; inevitable, because early views of the interpretation of Scripture did not allow for much latitude in the understanding of those texts which refer to the creation and structure of the world, and because the picture of the universe presented in the books of the Old Testament seemed to many in the early years of the Christian era to be a reasonable and consistent account of the actual universe. Although it would not be true to say that there was much interest or speculation on the exact manner of the physical structure and evolution of the universe in the early Church, it seems that the primitive biblical account of creation was considered satisfactory not only as an account of the relationship of God to man, but also as an actual description of the history of the physical creation of the universe. But the value of this description would not have been considered to lie in its directly cosmological aspects; interest in the manner of creation was not just a matter of intellectual curiosity about the world, as it might have been among the Greeks, but was directed to the discovery of the pattern of divine activity in the relation, not between God and the cosmos, but between God and man.

The sources of early Christian thinking on cosmology were not, of course, confined to the Hebrew world-picture of the Scriptures; many elements of the Greek, and particularly the Platonic, view of the universe appear in the

Fathers. But the primary and most important source was the Old Testament, and it is a matter of some importance to assess the creation narratives in Genesis both from the point of view of their origins and of their real significance. To do this it is necessary to consider briefly the structure of the early chapters of Genesis, and to say something about the literary form in which they are expressed.

The detailed studies of the books of the Pentateuch that have been made in the last hundred years with a critical approach to the text have produced a consensus of opinion that, although these books contain passages of widely differing character, they show signs of having been assembled and collated by a single hand. The application of literary criteria seems to show three main strands in the narrative, which are denoted by the use of the letters J, E and P. Assuming a long period in the history of the people of Israel during which the accounts in the Pentateuch were part of a purely oral tradition, it is considered that the J and E passages are from the early pre-exilic sources which were probably committed to writing in about the tenth century B.C. The letters J and E were originally used to denote the different sources as these are distinguished by the use of different words for the divine name, Yahweh (Jahweh) in the J passages and Elohim in the E passages. It is then thought that these two sources were combined at the time of the later monarchy and revised to give a version which reached its final form at the hands of a member of the priestly circle after the return from Babylon. These later and final contributions are denoted by the letter P.

There are in Genesis two distinct cosmogonic narratives. The more primitive is the J narrative (Gen. 2. 4b–25). In this, one is presented with the world as already existing as a waterless waste, which is barren because it has neither received rain nor is there a man to cultivate it. Then a fountain appears which rains down water; man is formed from the slime of the earth and placed in a paradise of pleasure. He is admonished not to eat of the tree of knowledge. The animals and birds are created and finally a woman is formed from one of the original man's ribs. The value of this narrative is clearly not cosmological, but it is interesting to note the connections with Babylonian thought on these matters, although the original waterless waste in which fertility is due to rain suggests Palestine rather than Mesopotamia where fertility is due to the over-flowing of the rivers. A sharp distinction between this story and the Babylonian mythologies is in the strict monotheism of the Hebrew account.

The P narrative (Gen. 1–2. 4a) is more valuable and in some ways differs quite radically from the J narrative. It presents a precise account of the later Hebrew cosmogony. God is described as having created heaven and earth, the earth being a watery chaos. With the creation of light one has night and day. This is the work of the first day. On the second day the waters are divided into those above and those below the firmament. Here one sees the Baby-lonian world picture, also referred to in Is. 40. 12–22 and Is. 45. 5–7, with the earth conceived of as resting on water, with a solid firmament supporting the waters above the earth. Above the firmament are the fixed stars and the paths of the sun and planets. Creation continues with the separa-tion of dry land, and so on for six days, each day seeing the creation of a particular set of objects, until the picture is completed by the creation of man.

It is quite obvious that these narratives are not written to be taken literally, if by this one means that they purport to give a physically accurate account of the things they describe. They do, of course, contain elements from the cosmology that had been absorbed into the Hebrew tradition during the time of strong Babylonian influence on Palestine, and these elements would have been considered as true by the writers. The creation they describe is the creation of the world as they believed it to exist, but what is also clear is that the actual structure of the world is not of primary concern to them, and their purpose in writing was not to present a detailed account of the physical properties of the universe. If they had wished to do this, they might have been able to do considerably better in the context of the Babylonian astronomy. Their aim was to present, using some of the mythological forms that were common property over much of the Near East at that time, an account of the first steps in the history of their people's relationship to God. In this respect the early chapters of Genesis are not different from any other part of the Pentateuch. They present the first step in the *Heilsgeschichte*, the history of salvation, and the Old Testament goes on to chronicle the religious history of the Jewish people from age to age.

So these first chapters of Genesis describe a real situation in symbolic terms. The symbolism is suited to a primitive people and its implications would be readily apparent to them. The reality it conveyed was the absolute dependence of the Jewish people on their God from the very earliest times, this dependence being due not only to his constant guidance of them, but also to the fact that he had created them and the entire universe. This is the real content of these passages. The literary form in which they are couched was the natural and obvious way to express this content to a people steeped in the symbolism it employed. A literal interpretation of these passages is not only impossible in the light of our present sophisticated knowledge of the universe, but also completely ignores the cultural context and literary tradition which produced them.

As has already been mentioned, the question of the origin and structure of the universe was not a matter for much discussion in the early Church. There was some controversy as to the length of the period of time referred to as a "day", during which so much seemed to have happened, but the chief interest in the early history of the world as described in Genesis centred on the account of the Fall, on the nature of women and so on. Augustine in his discussion of creation (*De Civitate Dei*, XII) stressed the fact of conservation in being, after an initial creation, as forming an essential part of a theological doctrine of creation. Two essential points in the continuing teaching of the Church on creation gradually appeared: that creation was from nothing and not from pre-existing matter, and that the universe had not existed from eternity but had a beginning in time.

The change in the world picture of medieval Europe with the revival of interest in Greek astronomy, and the importance of Aristotelean philosophy in the development of the new theology in the thirteenth century, led to a re-discussion of the problem. Aquinas, who used the Aristotelean cosmology, accepted the cosmogony of Genesis while allowing room for a difference of opinion as to the interpretation of the term "day". Perhaps more interesting in the context of modern controversy on the "age of the universe" which will be discussed in detail later, is his work *De Aeternitate Mundi*, where he argues that it is impossible to prove that the universe is finite in time without recourse to revelation.

How closely the Aristotelean cosmology had become linked with theological concepts was well shown by the Galileo affair in the early seventeenth century, which served to emphasize not only the difficulty of literal interpretation of the Scriptures, but also the hazards of a theology or philosophy depending on anything as ephemeral as a scientific theory. Forewarned by this example, and now more fully aware of the true nature of theological statements, modern theologians manage to avoid this obvious pitfall; but nevertheless talk of conflict between scientific theories and theology continues, and today this is particularly true of the science of cosmology.

INTERACTION BETWEEN COSMOLOGICAL AND THEOLOGICAL IDEAS

A great deal of the popular discussion of cosmology has centred on the concept of creation, which occurs in cosmological theories in two different contexts. There is the use of the term in the Steady-State theories to denote the continuous appearance of matter throughout the universe at such a rate as to keep the local density of matter constant, despite the general expansion of the universe. This has already been mentioned, as has the fact that this hypothesis is of a true creation of matter out of nothing, contradicting the Principle of Conservation of Matter and Energy. As in a theory of this type there is no reason why this process should not have gone on for all time, it has appeared to some that such a theory obviates the necessity for a creation at a finite time in the past. This is of course rather confused, as while such a process of continuous creation might have gone on for all time, one can certainly not argue directly from the theory that it must have gone on for all time. It has also been suggested that, as one now has the possibility of a mathematically formulated law describing the rate of creation, the mystery has in some way been taken out of creation.

There is another context in which creation occurs. In some of the so-called Evolutionary theories the expansion of the universe can be extrapolated back to a point in time when all the matter in the universe would have been collected in a comparatively small volume. This is of course the volume from which the expansion observed now originally took place. An assumption has been rashly made by some, including Sir Edmund Whittaker, that this dense state marks the beginning of the universe, and the start of the expansion in the past is to be in some sense identified with the moment of Creation. This offers the possibility of determining the age of the universe, that is, of dating Creation. It will be shown later that this possibility is illusory in principle. But Whittaker goes on to make this theory the basis of a proof for the existence of God. Although this is not an attack on theology, it is the sort of help that it is better without.

There is often a strong emotional response, from which sciences seem to be free, to some of these speculations. Hoyle's remark in a broadcast talk after a discussion of his Steady-State theory, "I am sure you would hardly wish me to end without saying something about how the New Cosmology affects me personally", is quite surprising, as one would not expect a scientific theory to affect anyone personally, in the sense of being a factor in a choice of a philosophy of life. It is, however, such personal reactions that have caused many of the confusions that arise in this subject. The following chapters will attempt to show both that there is in fact no reason for conflict between any of the ideas of cosmology and the traditional theology of Christianity, and, further, that cosmology, like any other physical science, can have nothing to say that might possibly cause such a conflict.

CHAPTER I

THE ASTRONOMICAL BACKGROUND TO COSMOLOGY

In order to understand the nature of the rival cosmological theories it is necessary to have some grasp of the observational evidence that they are all trying to account for, and which provides the possibility of testing their predictions. This evidence is, of course, drawn mainly from astronomical studies, although there are some results of conventional physics that are also relevant. This chapter is concerned mainly with our present knowledge of stars, of the galaxy and of the extragalactic nebulae, in so far as this knowledge is relevant to an understanding of the universe as a whole. It will be obvious that one is here concerned not with purely observational evidence but with an interpretation of observations in terms of more or less plausible theories. This is true of all the sciences but, as will become apparent, much of the astronomical theorizing relevant to cosmology is very uncertain, and it is perhaps well to bear in mind that confident statements on the nature of one or other astronomical object are often based on not very extensive observations which are perhaps also of questionable accuracy. An attempt will therefore be made to indicate the uncertainties, and to point out the more doubtful conclusions from the observations in so far as this is consistent with an elementary treatment of the subject.

A consistent and satisfactory picture of the main features of our astronomical environment has emerged over the past fifty years. We now know that the sun, the star of which the earth and planets are satellites, forms part of an enormous system of stars known as the Galaxy. This system, a crude hint of whose structure is given by the dense band of stars forming the Milky Way, is in the rough shape of a disc, somewhat fatter at its centre than at its edges, about 25 kiloparsecs in diameter and about 4 kiloparsecs in thickness, containing some 10^{11} stars.[1] The total mass of the matter in the Galaxy is of the order of 10^{11} times the mass of the sun, which itself has a mass of some 2×10^{33} grams. Despite this large mass only a very small fraction of the volume of the Galaxy is actually occupied by condensed matter; in fact, if all this mass were evenly distributed over the volume of the Galaxy the overall density would only be about 10^{-23} grams in every cubic centimetre or, assuming the matter to be all in the form of hydrogen atoms, only about four atoms in every cubic centimetre. So, in this local group of stars in which we find ourselves, the average density of matter is very low. Around the flat disc of stars, and extending beyond its limits, is a roughly spherically symmetric cloud of tight clusters of stars forming a halo around the main disc with a diameter of some 30 kiloparsecs, becoming less dense the further one goes from the centre of the Galaxy. Outside this halo system is virtually empty space.

[1] The astronomical unit of distance is the parsec, which is about 3×10^{18} centimetres. A kiloparsec is one thousand parsecs, while a megaparsec is one million parsecs.

This system of stars is by no means homogeneous. It has a distinct internal structure, and would, if seen by an observer viewing it perpendicularly to the plane of the disc, appear to be formed from a series of spiral arms radiating out from a central condensation, the spiral arms being formed from denser regions of stars associated with interstellar gas and dust. Our sun is situated in one of these spiral arms near the edge of the Galaxy. Nor are the stars of the Galaxy all of the same size, age, temperature or composition. While the sun appears to be some five thousand million years old, there are other stars with ages as short as a million years, and yet other objects which appear to be stars in the process of formation. Some stars show no trace of certain chemical elements which are very abundant in other stars; some are a thousand times more massive than others. Some do not shine with a constant brightness, but have regular or irregular changes in their energy output. Although we are far from understanding all the peculiarities of the behaviour of stars, and not at all certain of the explanation of some of their normal features, a broad picture of stellar structure and evolution is emerging, which is correlating the main observational data and suggesting a picture of the development of the Galaxy as a whole.

It was said above that the space outside the Galaxy is virtually empty. Although this is true for the region around the Galaxy to a distance of about 50 kiloparsecs from the galactic centre it is not true of extragalactic space as a whole. For at a distance of some 50 kiloparsecs are two other large conglomerations of stars called the Magellanic Clouds, and at a distance of about 570 kiloparsecs is the Andromeda Nebula which is a very similar structure to our own Galaxy in size and shape. These are three of the closest of the so-called extragalactic nebulae, stellar systems analogous to our own Galaxy, which are separated from one another by space with a vanishingly small density of matter compared with the density of matter within one of these systems. The extragalactic nebulae seem to be scattered throughout space in immense clusters; these clusters appear to contain anything from sixteen nebulae, as is the case with the Local Group containing our Galaxy, to 2500, as in the group seen in the constellation of Virgo. Each nebula within the group contains perhaps 10^{11} stars and has dimensions of perhaps as much as tens of kiloparsecs. Within the group the individual nebulae are some hundreds of kiloparsecs apart. A typical group will be about 3 megaparsecs across and a typical distance between adjacent groups would be some tens of megaparsecs.

The observable universe thus seems to be a collection of groups or clusters of nebulae. Further supergroups containing many ordinary groups may exist, but their existence is at present uncertain. The nebula we know best in many ways is the one in which we are embedded, and a study of cosmology can well begin with a study of the Galaxy.

THE GALAXY

The structure and dimensions of the Galaxy

One of the most important advances in astrophysics was the discovery of the two types of stellar population. In a series of researches on our Galaxy and on some extragalactic nebulae, Walter Baade came to the conclusion that the stars and the interstellar matter making up galaxies could be seen to belong to two roughly defined populations, these populations being defined by their physical properties. Population I, which makes up the spiral arms of the disc of our Galaxy and spiral arms in other galaxies, consists of an intimate mixture of stars and interstellar gas and dust in roughly equal proportions of stars and interstellar matter. Typical Population I objects are the very bright so-called supergiant stars, and the interstellar gas and dust clouds obscuring many parts of the Milky Way system. Population II on the other hand includes stars which are entirely free from any interstellar matter. The globular clusters forming the halo about the disc of our Galaxy and about many extragalactic nebulae are the extreme example of Population II. There is no trace of any gas or dust in between the stars of these clusters, and the very bright supergiant stars are absent. It should, however, be understood that there are many objects that are difficult to classify into one or the other of the stellar populations, and there appears a constant gradation between the two types.

There are more differences between the stellar populations than the two mentioned above, that is, the distinction between stars occurring in the spiral arms of the disc of galaxies and those occurring in the halo around the disc, and the distinction between stars associated with interstellar matter and those free from gas and dust. Ways have been found of determining both the compositions and the ages of stars and it appears that the Population I stars are rich in the heavy elements of the Periodic Table and young in age, while the stars of Population II are poor in heavy elements and relatively old. Furthermore, the two types have distinct dynamical properties. While the disc Population I stars generally have a low velocity perpendicular to the plane of the galactic disc, showing that their motions in the Galaxy are more or less confined to the disc itself, the halo Population II stars have relatively high velocities. There are then many ways of attempting to decide to which of the populations a given object belongs, and it will be shown how these properties are consistent with a model of the evolution of the Galaxy.

The knowledge that the spiral arm system of the Galaxy is formed from Population I objects gives us a hint as to how this system may be mapped out in detail. If a way can be found of mapping the distribution of the highly luminous supergiant stars or of the interstellar gas associated with the spiral arms, then one will have a picture of the spiral arm structure itself. Our best model of the structure of the disc of the Galaxy in fact comes from a method of detecting the interstellar gas. The hydrogen atoms in the interstellar gas have the property of emitting a very weak radio signal with a wavelength of 21 centimetres. As there is a great deal of hydrogen associated with the spiral arms, it is possible to detect this signal with an appropriate radio receiver.

There are two distinct pieces of information that can be extracted from these signals. When one is pointing the aerial of one's radio receiver in different directions corresponding to different lines of sight through the Galaxy, one finds both a different intensity in the received signal corresponding to a different number of hydrogen atoms in the line of sight, and a change in the wavelength of the signal due to the motions in the line of sight of the emitting atoms. This change of wavelength is due to the Doppler Effect; the wavelength of the signal from an atom moving away from us is longer than the wavelength of the signal from an atom which is moving towards us. Clearly the signals are quite difficult to interpret in terms of the spiral structure of the emitting hydrogen clouds. A high intensity in the signal in one direction may be due to the fact that one is observing one thick spiral arm or two thin spiral arms one behind the other. However, the shift in wavelength of the signals makes the interpretation somewhat easier. Together with other information about the rotational motions of the galactic disc, the spiral structure defined by the hydrogen gas can be gradually pieced together. From the intensity of the radio signals one can determine the amounts of hydrogen in the observable spiral arms, and from the changes in wavelength of the signals one can deduce the velocities of motion of the spiral arms as they rotate around the centre of the Galaxy.

What information has been obtained of spiral structure by the observation of the bright stars associated with the spiral arms goes to confirm the general picture offered by radio observations of the interstellar hydrogen gas. We are certainly embedded in a galaxy with a distinct spiral structure. But as yet nothing has been said on the problem of how to find the dimensions of this structure, although this information is in fact used in the interpretation of the radio observations.

The problem of determining distances in astronomy is one which is both technically and theoretically very difficult. Most of the techniques which will be referred to in this chapter are quite modern and stretch the capabilities of the best existing telescopes; they are also based on far-reaching assumptions and simplifications. These simplifications are necessary if one is to arrive at any conclusions about distance at all, but they must not be lost sight of in the complications of the theories and speculations based on them.

Ignoring the methods which have been used to find the dimensions of the Solar System, the first method to give any idea of astronomical distances was the method of trigonometrical parallax which is quite well suited to give relatively accurate distances of the brighter of the nearby stars. The principle of this method is quite simple. If one looks at an object close to one's eye against the background of a series of objects further away, a motion of one's eye from side to side causes the nearer object to move with respect to the more distant background. This is termed a motion of parallax and, knowing the distance one's eye has moved and the change of apparent position of the nearer object, one can deduce its distance. In the astronomical case the analogue of the motion of one's eye is the motion of the earth backwards and forwards in its orbit round the sun, and the motion of a nearby star is seen against the background of stars much further away. Knowing the dimensions of the earth's orbit and the change in the angular position of the nearby star relative to the background of stars one can determine its distance. A star which shifts through an angular distance of one second of arc as the earth travels round its orbit, i.e., which has a parallax of one second of arc, is said to be at a distance of 1 parsec. Unfortunately, this method can only be used to measure distance to stars which are closer to us than about 100 parsecs. For more distant stars the angular change in position is too small to be measured. However, the method can be used to give reliable distances which can be used to calibrate other methods of distance determination which can be used for more distant objects.

A further method is one which makes use of the proper motions of stars, the motion they show against the background of more distant stars due to their own intrinsic motions in the Galaxy. As the intrinsic motion of the sun is known from measurements of its velocity relative to the local group of surrounding stars using the Doppler shift in the frequency of lines in the spectra of these stars, a certain amount of the observed proper motion of the other stars will be due to the motion of the sun itself and this amount will depend on their distance. Once again one uses the principle of parallax, but in this case one must approach the problem statistically, considering large numbers of stars. One cannot be sure that this method is able to give individual distances accurately, but it does offer the possibility of determining rough distances for groups of stars beyond the limit of the method of trigonometrical parallax, up to a distance of perhaps a kiloparsec. Bearing in mind that the diameter of the Galaxy is about 25 kiloparsecs, this method is only of use in our immediate neighbourhood and something further is needed if we are to measure distances in the Galaxy as a whole.

The above methods give us a large number of distances which can be used to establish some sort of correlation between the absolute brightness of stars and other properties they may possess. From the apparent brightness in the sky of a particular star and from a knowledge of its distance one can deduce its absolute brightness. And there are in general two properties of stars that can in some way be related to their absolute brightness, the character of their spectra and, in some cases, the character of a possible periodic variation in their brightness. This is something that cannot be properly understood without an introduction to the system of stellar classification. There are two classifications that are relevant here; that into spectral type and that into luminosity.

On the basis of the consideration of the spectra of stars they can be divided into a series of spectral types that give a rough indication of the stellar temperature. Then each spectral type can be subdivided to make the classification more precise. The hottest stars have spectral type O. These show in their spectra lines due to the helium atom with one of its electrons removed, which indicate temperatures of some tens of thousands of degrees Centigrade. The B stars are somewhat cooler, and lines of ordinary helium are prominent. In the A stars the temperature has dropped to about 10,000°C, and the lines of hydrogen are dominant. F stars show weaker hydrogen lines with the lines of some heavy elements, while in spectral type G (which includes our sun) the surface temperature has dropped to about 5,000°C. The later types K and M are cooler still, and begin to show spectral lines of molecules quite strongly, indicating their lower temperatures. This series of spectral types is also characterized by the colour of the stars. O and B stars are white, later types yellow, and the K and M stars are red; this is an obvious indication of the drop of temperature along the sequence. This colour is amenable to precise measurement. If the brightness (or magnitude[2]) is measured through two filters which only allow relatively narrow bands of the spectrum to be transmitted in two different regions of the spectrum, the difference in magnitude can be used to define the colour index, which is a precise measurement of the colour of a star.

Stars do not, however, differ only in their surface temperatures or colours. They also differ in the total outflow of radiant energy from their surfaces. A larger star will radiate more energy than a smaller star of the same surface temperature. So a classification into stars with a greater or lesser energy output, or luminosity, will be a classification into larger or smaller size and mass. There are six recognized luminosity classes. Class I of supergiants; II of bright giants; III of giants; IV of subgiants; V of dwarfs; and VI of subdwarfs and white dwarfs. Some of these classes are shown in the diagram (Fig. I) which is a plot of absolute magnitude against colour index for a sample of Population I stars. It will be seen that the stars are confined to relatively small regions of the diagram. Such a diagram can be compiled from stars of absolute

[2] The measure of brightness is the stellar *magnitude*, the brightness on a logarithmic scale.

magnitude determined perhaps from a trigonometrical parallax, and known spectral type, and can then be used to derive the absolute magnitude of stars whose spectral type is known, and whose luminosity class can be recognized from features in their spectra. A star whose spectral type or colour index places it in the right-hand side of the

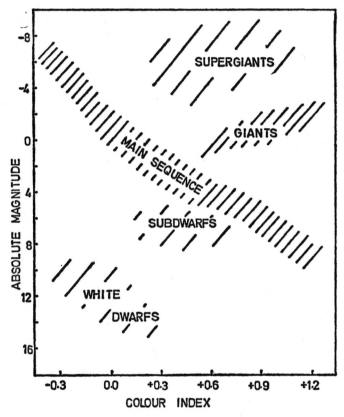

Fig. 1. Plot of absolute magnitude against colour index for Population I stars

diagram, say at colour index $+0.8$, could be either a giant or a dwarf[3] with quite different absolute magnitudes. If its luminosity class can be determined from its spectrum, from features characteristic of the conditions in its surface due to its size, then it can be placed unambiguously in the diagram and its absolute magnitude determined. Then if its apparent magnitude is known its distance can be found.

This is a method of distance measurement which is suitable for much larger distances than those previously described. It has, however, several drawbacks. It assumes that there is no absorption of the light of the star by any interstellar matter that may lie between us and the star. This is not in general true, and methods have been devised to correct for the influence of interstellar absorption on the star's magnitude and colour index. However, there are large regions of the Galaxy where the absorption is so strong that this method of distance determination is impracticable.

It was mentioned above that there might also be a correlation between the absolute brightness of a star and some variable characteristic. In fact there is a close correlation between absolute magnitude and the period of variation in brightness for a large class of stars whose brightness varies with a regular period. The first variable stars to be used as distance indicators were the Cepheid variables, intrinsically bright stars that vary in brightness with individual periods of variation between two and forty days. A number of these stars are visible in the extragalactic system known as the Large Magellanic Cloud. As this system is some 50 kiloparsecs from us and is less than 10 kiloparsecs in diameter, all the stars in it can be considered to be at roughly the same distance. If one

[3] The dwarf stars are those which lie along the Main Sequence in Fig. I.

observes both the apparent magnitudes and the periods of the Cepheid variables in the Large Magellanic Cloud one finds a definite relation between the two. If now one can find some way of converting these apparent magnitudes to absolute magnitudes one can find the distance of any other Cepheid variable by measuring its period of variation, finding its absolute magnitude from the known relation between magnitude and period, and deducing its distance from its apparent magnitude. The relation between absolute and apparent magnitude was found by applying the statistical parallax method to Cepheid variables in our Galaxy.

The first use of Cepheid variables to measure distance in this way was by Shapley, who found the distances of a few halo globular clusters which contained Cepheid variables. Unfortunately this work was done before the distinction had been made between the two stellar populations. The Cepheid variables used in the Large Magellanic Cloud were Population I objects. As has been mentioned, the globular cluster stars are Population II objects, and the Cepheid-like variables in them (now known as W Virginis variables) do not obey the same absolute magnitude-period relation as the Population I Cepheids. Luckily, however, a correction for interstellar absorption, which Shapley omitted to make, almost compensates for this confusion, and the distances he measured to the globular clusters are not far wrong. This method of distance measurement leads to another. Most of the globular clusters contain another type of variable star, RR Lyrae variables, with absolute magnitudes that can be calibrated by the Cepheid variables. These can in turn be used to give the distance of those globular clusters which contain no Cepheid variables, but do contain RR Lyrae variables.

Having found the distances of the clusters containing variables, one can then look for other criteria of absolute magnitude among stars of the clusters. Shapley formed a method of determining the distances of the clusters both by using the magnitude of the brightest star in the cluster, and another method depending on the diameters of the clusters as a whole. Both of these methods are calibrated by using the distances found from the RR Lyrae variables. This illustrates very well a characteristic of astronomical distance measurement that will become even more apparent when dealing with the distances of the extragalactic objects. With the help of a first method, one calibrates a further method which is applicable when the first method is inapplicable. In the case of the globular clusters, first the absolute magnitude-period relationship of the Cepheids was calibrated by the use of the method of statistical parallax; then the Cepheids were used in turn to calibrate the RR Lyrae variables which can be used when no Cepheids are present; finally the RR Lyrae variables calibrate the brightest star and the diameter criteria, which can be used when no RR Lyrae variables are present. Clearly the errors accumulate with each successive link in the chain, but unfortunately this kind of approach is the only one possible.

Shapley then used his globular cluster distances to get some idea of the dimensions of the Galaxy as a whole. Assuming that the globular clusters form a roughly spherical halo around the disc, one can find the centre of this sphere and the distance to this centre is the distance from us to the centre of the Galaxy. For a variety of reasons Shapley over-estimated the distance. Fortunately, we now have more reliable methods of calibrating the RR Lyrae stars. One proceeds by drawing a diagram similar to that in Fig. I for the stars of a globular cluster, entering the RR Lyrae variables in the diagram, plotting apparent magnitude against colour index. Theoretically one expects the cool dwarf stars to occupy the region they occupy in

Fig. I. Thus by adjusting the globular cluster diagram vertically until the cool dwarf stars of both diagrams coincide, one can read off the absolute magnitude of the cluster variables.

A very interesting and important use of these stars to find the distance to the galactic centre is due to Baade. It is known that the galactic centre is in the direction of the constellation Sagittarius, and it is thought that the disc of the Galaxy has a bulge near its centre. Baade chose a field of stars in this direction, surrounding the globular cluster NGC 6522. He then counted the number of RR Lyrae variables in this field and plotted a diagram of the number of variables of a given apparent brightness against the brightness. There is in this diagram a very distinct peak showing a great concentration of the variables in a small volume. Assuming that this is the galactic centre, and knowing the absolute magnitude of the variables, one can find, after correcting for interstellar absorption, the distance to the galactic centre. Baade found the distance to be just over 8 kiloparsecs.

The above will have given some idea of how one approaches the problem of finding the structure and dimensions of the Galaxy. Later it will become apparent that our Galaxy is a quite average galaxy both as regards shape and size. It is now of interest to see roughly how one can determine the nature of the material from which it is formed, and how the variations of composition among stars suggest possible modes of stellar evolution, which lead to the calculation of stellar ages and then to an age for the Galaxy as a whole.

The composition and age of the Galaxy

It is now possible to make fairly accurate estimates of the abundance of the elements in most types of stars. The normal stellar spectrum of an element is an absorption spectrum, that is, the spectral lines of the element are dark lines on the background of the continuous radiation of the star. Elements in stars are identified by comparing the wavelengths and intensities of the stellar lines with the wavelengths and intensities of lines of the element produced in some way in laboratory light sources. Once an element has been proved present in a star, its abundance in the star can in favourable cases be calculated from the strength of its lines and from a knowledge of the structure of the atmosphere of the star where the lines are produced. There are now quite detailed analyses of the solar atmosphere and of other stars whose atmospheres are understood. The general outline of the variation of the abundance of elements among stars is gradually emerging. The great bulk of the matter in most stars is in the form of hydrogen, which is clearly the most abundant element in the universe. The next most abundant element is the next heaviest in the Periodic Table, helium. These two elements between them make up all but less than 1 per cent of the number of atoms in a typical star. The elements heavier than helium are thus rather rare, but their presence has quite a profound effect on the star's behaviour. There is a clear distinction between the two stellar populations in heavy element abundance. Population II stars being significantly poorer in the heavy elements than Population I stars.

There has been developed recently a theory of the origin of the elements which can account for the broad lines of the abundance difference between stars, and to appreciate the basis of this theory something must be said about the general problem of the origin and evolution of stars. Let us consider the formation of a galactic cluster, one of the star groupings quite common in the Population I spiral arm structure of the Galaxy, containing, say, a hundred stars in a region some 10 parsecs across. These would appear to be stars with a common origin. One assumes that they were formed by the contraction of a large diffuse cloud of interstellar gas (mainly hydrogen) and dust under the influence of the gravitational attraction between the particles of the cloud. As the cloud shrinks gradually it breaks up into fragments which continue to contract individually. As these clouds get smaller and smaller, the potential energy of the gravitational field is converted into thermal energy, and by the time each cloud has contracted into an object of the size and density of a star the temperature in its interior is very high, of the order of a million degrees Centigrade. Now this temperature is high enough for reactions to occur between the nuclei of the atoms of the star, and these reactions start to produce energy which passes through the material of the star and emerges partly in the form of visible light. So from the original cloud of gas we have a series of stars of differing masses, as the original fragments will not have been all of the same size, and differing brightnesses, the brightness depending on the mass, forming a close association in space, the galactic cluster.

To know how the stars will evolve after their contraction from the interstellar material, we must consider the nature of the nuclear reactions that determine their energy output and the changes in these reactions that produce variations in the properties of the star. The change in the observable properties of the star is well seen in a diagram similar to Fig. I which plots the brightness of the star against its special type of colour index. Fig. II is such a diagram for a typical galactic cluster. After their initial contraction the stars settle on the line marked Main Sequence. Their positions on this line are determined by their original masses;

the larger masses are at the top of the Main Sequence and
are hot and blue; the smaller masses are at the bottom and
are cool and red. It can be shown theoretically that a
series of contracting stars will in fact lie eventually on the
Main Sequence. Our first problem is to see why the

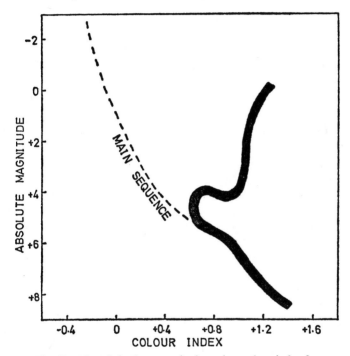

Fig. II.   Plot of absolute magnitude against colour index for a
galactic cluster (thick line)

observed stars of galactic clusters do not in general all lie
along this line. The observed stars for an actual cluster are
shown by the thick line. Many of them are considerably
redder than Main Sequence stars of the same brightness

and only the smaller, fainter stars lie on the Main Sequence in the positions they occupied after their original formation.

The thermonuclear reaction that initially provides the energy of the young star is one which converts the hydrogen nuclei into helium nuclei. The hydrogen nucleus is formed of one proton, while that of helium is formed of two protons and two neutrons. At the very high temperatures in stellar interiors helium nuclei can be built up from hydrogen nuclei. The end product of the chain of reactions is found to be slightly less in mass than the constituents that went to build it. The helium nucleus of four nuclear particles has a smaller mass than the four hydrogen nuclei that have been destroyed in its production. This difference in mass appears as the energy of the reaction products and much of this energy is transformed into the radiant energy that appears at the surface of the star. Such nuclear reactions can continue as long as the conditions in the interior of the star are appropriate to them. Clearly the continual conversion of hydrogen into helium is going to result in a gradual increase in the proportion of helium in the centre of the star, but initially this does not have a very significant effect on the star's observable properties. It is not considered that the helium produced at the star's centre is dissipated throughout the star to reach its surface. It is confined to a small core at the centre which begins to form when the star has consumed about 10 per cent of its original hydrogen content, and a different series of nuclear reactions have set in to convert further hydrogen to helium.

It is with this new series of reactions due to the gradual increase in temperature and helium content that the structure of the star begins to change radically. The helium-rich core starts to contract and the temperature in the region immediately surrounding it rises and becomes the main source of energy production. The radius of the star as a whole now begins to increase, and as the rate of energy generation does not increase fast enough to keep up the star's surface temperature, the stellar surface cools and the star becomes redder, moving off the Main Sequence towards the right in Fig. II. Now the more massive the star the more rapidly does this series of processes take place, so that the stars initially near the top of the Main Sequence move off towards the right of the diagram before the smaller stars near the bottom of the diagram. The positions of the observed stars in the diagram show this. Assuming that all the stars of the cluster were formed simultaneously at some time in the distant past, only the more massive ones have been able to form helium-rich cores at their centres, while the less massive ones have not yet evolved so far and retain their initial positions on the Main Sequence. As time goes on one expects the point in the diagram where the stars have just moved off to the right of their initial positions to move gradually down the Main Sequence to smaller and smaller stars.

Thus the younger a cluster is, the more stars it has near their initial positions. A very old cluster will have only a few of its smallest stars still on the Main Sequence, while a fully evolved cluster may have none at all. There is an obvious application of this to the possibility of dating the different clusters from the point at which the stars start to turn away from the Main Sequence. This point will correspond to the conversion of a certain proportion of their hydrogen to helium, and if the rates of the various reactions bringing this about can be found, one can find an age for the cluster as a whole from the time of its formation. We will return to this point later, but it is of some interest now to follow the evolutionary process further. As the helium-rich core expands with the gradual destruction of hydrogen there comes a point, when half of the stellar material is in the core, at which the properties of the core material change in such a way that temperatures of some 10^8 degrees Centigrade are reached. At these temperatures the helium nuclei themselves interact to build even heavier elements with a considerable production of energy. In these reactions carbon, oxygen, neon and magnesium are formed. When the helium itself is exhausted in these processes, the stellar core contracts and its temperature rises still further to about 10^9 degrees Centigrade. Now the neon, carbon and oxygen are partially destroyed but their disintegration fragments react with other nuclei to build up silicon and sulphur. All the time the star as a whole is becoming brighter and larger, moving into the top right-hand corner of Fig. II. When the core temperature rises to about 3×10^9 degrees, the evolution of the star becomes very rapid and the rate of formation of new elements by the thermonuclear reactions in the core is speeded up. The iron group elements are formed in stars where the core is so hot that a statistical equilibrium exists between the free protons and neutrons and the nuclei. The further evolution of such a star is in an explosion which redistributes the newly formed heavy elements among the interstellar matter of the Galaxy. Such explosions seem to occur in the stars known as supernovae which increase very rapidly to brightness and then decay. A more normal evolutionary path is thought to be back across the diagram to the region of white dwarf stars which are very small and appear to represent the end point of stellar evolution.

So the theory of stellar evolution explains not only the rough features of how stellar properties change as they age, but also provides an explanation of the origin of the elements. These are produced from the original hydrogen from which the star contracted and are returned to the interstellar medium by means of stellar explosions or by other forms of ejection of matter from evolved stars. Clearly what one may call second-generation stars may condense from material which has previously been enriched by an earlier passage through the centre of a star. This may explain the high heavy element abundance of young Population I stars in contrast to the low heavy element abundance of old Population II stars, the Population II stars having condensed directly from the matter contracting to form the Galaxy as a whole, while the Population I stars are condensed from matter which has undergone progressive enrichment with heavy elements in one or more cycles of stellar evolution.

It will be useful to summarize the results of age determinations of stars based on the theory of stellar evolution by the method sketched previously for a few types of stars in the Galaxy, to gain some idea as to the age of the Galaxy itself. The youngest galactic cluster to have been dated from the position of deviation from the initial Main Sequence is only about a million years old. The oldest yet observed appears to be NGC 188 with an age of about 15×10^9 years. The age of the oldest stars in our immediate neighbourhood is even greater, about 20×10^9 years. The oldest globular clusters in the galactic halo are perhaps 25×10^9 years old. It should be noted that these "ages" denote the lapse of time since the stars became sufficiently condensed for the conversion of hydrogen into helium in their interiors to supply the energy lost by radiation from their surfaces.

It cannot be sufficiently stressed how uncertain these age estimates are. Since the theory was sufficiently developed to make such estimates feasible their values have been constantly revised. The possibility of their being in error by a factor of two can by no means be excluded. But one can be confident as to the order of magnitude they provide. One would certainly not expect the Galaxy to be younger than 10^{10} years. There are quite independent age estimates of objects in the Galaxy that are consistent with these ages of stars. An object that can be very accurately dated is the earth. Radioactive minerals such as uraninite and monazite may be dated by a quantitative analysis of the radioactive isotopes they contain and of the disintegration products of these isotopes. Since the rates at which lead is generated by the decay of thorium and two isotopes of uranium are known, it is possible to determine the time required for the accumulation of the lead now present in any radioactive mineral which has been analysed for lead, thorium and uranium. Assuming the mineral was free from lead at the time of its formation, and that it has remained undisturbed ever since, then the time so calculated is the true age of the mineral. These conditions are, however, rarely fulfilled, and the effects of any lead originally present, and of any dissipation of the end products must be assessed. The techniques of separate analysis of the isotopes of lead have made such an assessment easier. The greatest age found by these methods is about 5×10^9 years for the time since when the earth's mantle had sufficiently solidified to preserve heterogeneities in its composition.

Similar methods have been used to date meteorites, and similar ages obtained. It is of interest to note that an estimate of the age of the moon from the effects of tidal friction gives an age close to that of the earth and the meteorites. So one can have some confidence in an age of about 5×10^9 years for the Solar System. This is about a fifth of the greatest age suggested for globular cluster stars, which seems not unreasonable.

Attempts have been made to use the dynamics of stellar motion to obtain age estimates. Jeans' early investigations led to a time-scale for the Galaxy of 10^{12} to 10^{13} years, but have now been discredited. The value of some of the later methods is lessened by the doubtful nature of some of the simplifications introduced. Nevertheless, they are of interest in showing rough independent confirmation of other age estimates. The theory of comparatively dense clusters of stars has been developed by Chandrasekhar. These clusters are gradually disrupted, not by individual stars being dragged out by the gravitational attraction of stars outside the cluster, but by interactions among the cluster stars themselves. If a star in the cluster by means of gravitational interaction with the other stars attains a high enough velocity it will be able to escape from the cluster. As time goes on, star after star attains this escape velocity and leaves the cluster. Chandrasekhar calculated how long this process would take to disrupt a galactic cluster such as the Pleiades, and found a period of about 3×10^9 years. On the other hand, the life of a much denser structure, such as a globular cluster, would be of the order of 10^{12} years. All the galactic clusters on this theory would dissolve in periods of some 3×10^9 years, and the argument goes that as there are still plenty of galactic clusters that have not dissolved, the Galaxy must have a similar time-scale. There seems no reason, however, why galactic clusters should not be continually forming, indeed there is direct evidence of very young clusters. But bearing in mind the simplifications that must be introduced into such theories to make a solution mathematically possible, it is gratifying that the maximum ages they give for such clusters are of the same order of magnitude as those obtained by other methods.

There is a further method of dating the Galaxy, or rather, finding a minimum age for it, that uses the theory of the origin of the elements in stars. Assuming the Galaxy to have originated from a cloud of almost pure hydrogen, the elements such as uranium that occur terrestrially must have been produced by thermonuclear reactions in stars since the formation of the Galaxy. Now the uranium isotopes are thought to have been formed in a type of supernova explosion which scattered them into the interstellar medium, from which in due course they were condensed into a second or later generation of stars. From the theory one knows the relative amounts of the two uranium isotopes that have originally been produced in the stellar explosion. Now one also knows the rate at which each isotope decays, so from their present relative abundances on the earth one can calculate the time of their formation, which appears to be about 7×10^9 years ago. This is on the assumption that the uranium which is found on earth is the product of only one synthesis in a star, of only one supernova explosion. But it might well have been processed in a series of such stars before it finally condensed into the Solar System. In such a case one can repeat the calculation for the formation of the two isotopes, now in a series of supernovae, and one finds an age for uranium isotopes of between about 12 and 7×10^9 years. This is clearly only a minimum age for the Galaxy. A great deal could have happened before the formation of the uranium that we now have on the earth.

The conclusion one can draw from all the above work is that the Galaxy as a whole is probably about 20×10^9 years old. The oldest objects in it are the globular cluster stars of the extended halo, while among the youngest are the stars that are at present in the course of formation in the galactic disc. It is now of interest to consider what light all our knowledge of the structure, composition and age of the Galaxy throws on its origin; then one can compare it with the other extragalactic stellar systems that are more or less similar to it.

The origin and evolution of the Galaxy

When we spoke of the origin of stars in the Galaxy we referred to them as being formed in groups or clusters. The original cloud from which a cluster is formed contracts and fragments to give a number of stars of differing masses but a common origin. There is an analogous process in the formation of whole galaxies. It has been remarked that the extragalactic nebulae, the galaxies outside our own, occur in groups. Our Galaxy is situated in the Local Group of sixteen galaxies, a system centred on a point about 400 kiloparsecs from us. This Local Group is some 11 megaparsecs from the closest neighbouring cluster of galaxies, the Virgo Group, which is a much larger array of some 2,500 galaxies. These groups are the analogues of stellar clusters. They contain galaxies of common origin and age although perhaps quite different mass, size and shape. There is evidence that star formation started at about the same time in all the galaxies of the Local Group, which supports this point; and members of the group are held together, as are the stars of a cluster, by gravitational attraction.

There is, however, a significant difference between the contraction of the stars of a cluster from the original gas cloud, and the contraction of whole galaxies from the supercloud that gives rise to a group or galaxies. While the stellar cluster cloud fragments into stars, the turbulence in the contracting supercloud fragments it into pieces which themselves are further subdivided, and galaxies are formed by the gradual attachment of smaller pieces to one another. The rotational property of the Galaxy is explained by the original relative motions of the constituent pieces, and the more compact the Galaxy became, the more marked would be the effect of its original angular momentum; the flatness of the disc is a result of this rotation. The spiral structure of the Galaxy is best considered by comparison with the structure of other galaxies discussed in the following pages.

A piece of evidence that our Galaxy has in fact collapsed from the much larger volumes of gas originally forming it is given by the shape of the spherical halo formed around the disc by the globular clusters and the variable stars that move between the clusters. The halo stars form a sphere that must at one time have been filled by the material of the collapsing Galaxy. They move in highly eccentric orbits with very high components of velocity towards the plane of the disc. This is well explained if they were indeed formed as the Galaxy collapsed and retained the original motions of the turbulent contracting cloud towards the centre of the Galaxy. The hypothesis that they were thus formed before the disc had contracted to its present size is supported by their great ages in comparison with the Population I stars of the disc, and by the fact that they do not have the high heavy element abundances of the disc stars. These extreme Population II objects thus appear to be a relic of a time before the Galaxy had settled down to its present configuration, and before the processes of synthesis of elements in stellar interiors had time to enrich with the heavy elements the original material from which the Galaxy contracted.

THE EXTRAGALACTIC NEBULAE

The structure and distribution of the nebulae

There are four different general types of galaxies in a classification depending on their structures. The elliptical nebulae (Type E) range from circular or globular objects to elongated ellipses. As a rule they show no structural details apart from a general decrease in brightness from the centre to the edges. There are subdivisions of this type depending on the degree of deviation from the spherical shape. The normal spiral nebulae (Type S) show the characteristic spiral arms emerging from a bright central nucleus. In the most regular examples of this class only two arms emerge from the nucleus and they are wrapped symmetrically about the centre. One defines sub-types by the relative importance of the central nucleus and the degree of unwinding of the arms. The spiral arm structure is of bright Population I stars and clouds of interstellar hydrogen and dust. A surrounding halo of Population II objects is often seen. The barred spirals (Type SB) show a more or less prominent nucleus crossed by a bar, from the extremities of which the spiral arms originate. The various sub-types of the S and SB nebulae account for 80 per cent of observed nebulae. The highly amorphous Magellanic Clouds are examples of the final, rather rare, class of irregular nebulae (Type I) which show no trace of spiral structure or of a central nucleus.

These various types, all of widely differing sizes, occur jumbled together in the different groups of galaxies, but there are a few galaxies that appear to be scattered between the groups and to exist independently of them. It appears to be the rule, however, that galaxies exist generally in the groups and those situated outside groups are exceptions.

While the relatively loose groups of galaxies seem to contain all the different structural types the tighter, more compact, groups have a predominance of the elliptical type. This can be explained by the more frequent gravitational encounters between galaxies in the denser groups, with a consequent removal of the more extended parts of the galaxies. Such encounters would be expected to increase the amount of matter between the galaxies and to reduce the number of extended spiral systems, leaving them in the tighter elliptical form. In fact the intergalactic material produced in such processes is observable, and most of the luminous component of it is condensed into stars of Population I, indicating that it probably arose in the outer spiral arm structure of earlier spiral galaxies.

A result of some importance to cosmology comes from a comparison of the nearer groups with those further away. As the light that we receive from the more distant objects has travelled further than the light from nearby objects, we see the more distant objects as they were at some time in the past corresponding to the time their light has taken to reach us. We do not see, therefore, all the observable galaxies at the same time in their history; we see distant galaxies in the distant past, and nearer galaxies in the more recent past relative to ourselves. So a simple examination and intercomparison of objects of widely differing distances gives us a chance of intercomparing objects of widely differing ages. Now if the groups of galaxies belong to an evolving universe one might expect some difference to be observable between the distant, younger groups and the closer and older groups. One can look for different criteria of evolution in the groups; for differences in structure, in the average number of galaxies in the groups, in the types of galaxy, or in the characteristics of the stars they contain. An extremely important conclusion from this kind of investigation, due to Zwicky, is that the compact clusters of galaxies seem to contain roughly the same number of galaxies at all distances and times, and that their shape and the distribution of galaxies within them also seem unchanged in time. More will be said of this kind of observation in the next chapter.

A further interesting conclusion of optical work on clusters of galaxies is that there appears to be no evidence that the groups are themselves organized into super-groups. There thus appears to be no evidence as yet for a "hierarchical" universe, with galaxies formed in groups which themselves form larger groups and so on. The reason for this is not clear, but it will be one of the tasks of cosmology to explain it. Furthermore, the groups seem to be scattered fairly evenly over the sky; one sees approximately the same number in whatever direction one looks, taking into account possible obscuration due to galactic or extragalactic material in the line of sight.

Nothing has yet been said about the methods used in determining the distances of the extragalactic nebulae. It will be seen that the methods used inside the Galaxy can often be used to find distances outside it, in particular the use of variable stars. As has been mentioned, the short-period variable stars of the RR Lyrae type can be used to find reliable series of distances to the globular clusters of the galactic halo, calibrating their absolute magnitudes from their position in a plot of magnitude against colour index. Unfortunately these stars are not intrinsically bright enough to be of much use as distance indicators in other galaxies. They can, however, be used to fix the absolute magnitudes of the Population II Cepheids that occur in the same globular clusters, to give a relation between the period of light variation of these much brighter stars and their absolute magnitudes. If, therefore, such stars can be detected in extragalactic nebulae there is some hope of their use as distance indicators. The same applies to the classical Cepheids of Population I if a correct relation between their periods and absolute magnitudes can be found. There are other objects in the Galaxy whose absolute luminosity can be found with some degree of accuracy. If similar objects can be identified in other galaxies these too can be used for distance determination. Novae, stars whose brightness increases rapidly and then fades gradually away, are among these. So are the very bright supergiant stars and the planetary nebulae. One assumes, of course, that similar objects in all galaxies have similar luminosities.

We shall describe some of the methods that have been used to find the distance of the Andromeda nebula, as a great deal of work has been done on this problem which is of great interest in fixing the distance scale of the universe. As this galaxy is fairly near it is possible to observe the globular clusters that form a halo round the disc. One does not attempt to resolve individual stars in the clusters but determines the apparent magnitudes of the clusters as a whole. One finds the average apparent magnitude and knowing the average absolute magnitude for globular clusters, from those observed in our Galaxy for which distances are available from the methods described, one can find a distance to the Andromeda nebula. The distance obtained by observing periods of classical Cepheids agrees roughly with this. Hubble has observed a considerable number of novae in this nebula. Comparing their luminosity when they have reached their maximum brightness with the luminosity of novae in the Galaxy of known distance in a similar stage of their evolution one can again find the distance of the Andromeda nebula. Similarly, planetary nebulae give a distance determination. One can then use the value for the distance of this nebula to find the absolute magnitude for the nebula as a whole. Similar work on nearby galaxies leads one to an idea of how intrinsically bright a whole galaxy is. With this information one can find rough distances to galaxies too far away for individual objects to be observed in them.

A criterion which can be applied to somewhat more distant galaxies is that based on the brightness of the brightest stars they contain, if these stars can be resolved. By observing the brightest stars in the Magellanic Clouds one can find their absolute magnitudes from the known distances of the Clouds, and by comparing these absolute magnitudes with others obtained from nearby galaxies get some idea of the average brightness of these objects. Other bright objects in galaxies, which were at one time confused with the brightest stars, are the H II regions, which are large volumes of ionized hydrogen. One can find the average angular size of these regions in the nearer galaxies and then use their apparent angular size in more distant galaxies for distance determination. This type of work will lead one to assign an average absolute magnitude to galaxies as a whole. There is unfortunately quite a large spread in the brightness of galaxies, and there is the further complication that in looking at more distant galaxies one may be looking at systematically younger objects with quite different luminosities. A criterion used by Hubble to find distances to remote clusters of galaxies was to assume that the twenty brightest members of the clusters have on average the same absolute magnitude in all clusters. This of course disregards all differences between individual clusters as well as possible effects of evolution. Research seems to indicate that this is a valid criterion, and it is valuable in that it can be used for the furthest visible clusters.

It is by such methods that one tries to build up a scale

of distances to the limits of observation of one's telescopes. Local distances are more reliable than distances to remoter objects, and the latter are dependent on the former. The progressive method of distance determination, starting with nearby objects and working to the most distant, is the only one possible in astronomy. The reliability of the methods is rapidly increasing, but we already have a distance-scale of the universe which tells us that two thousand megaparsecs will not take us to its visible limit. And much of this is based on a distance minute by comparison, the distance of the earth from the sun.

Radio sources and the nebulae

We have already mentioned the emission and absorption of radio waves by the neutral hydrogen gas in our Galaxy at a wavelength of 21 centimetres. This neutral hydrogen is not, however, the only source of radio waves. There are small discrete sources scattered throughout the Galaxy that emit at other radio wavelengths. An example of such a "radio star" is the Crab nebula, which is one of the strongest sources of radio waves in the sky. This nebula is the remnant of a violent supernova explosion which occurred in the eleventh century and was observed by a number of Chinese astrologers. The radio emission is due to so-called synchrotron radiation by the very energetic electrons remaining from the explosion moving in the weak magnetic field of the nebula. Such discrete galactic sources are distributed at random throughout the Galaxy and form a flattened disc system similar to that formed by optical objects. There is, however, another class of radio sources which appear to be distributed more uniformly over the sky. This suggests that they are not part of the Galaxy itself, but are scattered more or less isotropically through the space outside it.

We can in fact observe 21-centimetre radiation due to the neutral hydrogen in some other galaxies. This is not surprising as they have many other features similar to ours, such as spiral structure or an analogous mixture of the stellar populations. The Andromeda nebula, our nearest neighbour from among the elliptical galaxies, emits a wide spectrum of radio waves. For this and similar galaxies there appears to be about the same ratio between the intensity of emission in the radio region of the spectrum and the optical wavelengths that we observe in our own. The 21-centimetre line is observed in the Andromeda nebula, and shifts in its wavelength give a clue as to its internal motions in much the same way as we inferred motions in our Galaxy from similar shifts, interpreting them in terms of the Doppler Effect. But there are only a comparatively small number of galaxies observable at radio wavelengths that have what we may call this normal behaviour. There are many more sources that behave quite differently; these are the very intense and very distant *radio galaxies*, which are the sources that are of greater importance for a study of the large-scale aspects of the universe.

It must be pointed out that a great difficulty in this branch of radio astronomy is the identification of these very strong extragalactic sources with any optically visible object, as it is only after such identifications have been made that one can determine the distances of the sources and so get some idea as to their absolute strength. This is largely due to the low resolving power of existing radio telescopes, that is, to their poor ability to discriminate between two close sources that would be optically clearly distinguishable. A radio astronomer can only determine a comparatively rough position for a source, and the area of the sky which he can define as the approximate position may contain several optical objects, any of which could be the source of the radio waves. Some identifications of radio sources have, however, been made with distant galaxies.

It is very difficult to define one property of a galaxy that would identify it optically as one of these radio galaxies. A wide variety of types of galaxy have been found to emit strongly in the radio region of the spectrum. Double galaxies, which are two galaxies in close proximity, account for some of the most intense sources, but sometimes single elliptical or spherical galaxies are found to be radio galaxies. One factor that seems common to all is large size and high luminosity. It has also been found that the volume from which the radio emission originates is always larger than the apparent optical size of the galaxy. Furthermore, sometimes a single galaxy is associated with two radio sources, or a double galaxy with a single source; and the shape of the radio emitter and the associated galaxy is often widely different. One of the strongest of the radio galaxies is Cygnus A, which appears optically to be not a single galaxy, but two galaxies partly compenetrating. Whether it is two galaxies in collision or two galaxies in the process of separating from one another is not yet known.

The importance of these objects lies in the fact that being intrinsically such strong emitters of radio waves they are detectable at very great distances and can be used to explore the most distant parts of the universe. The sort of information that they can give us may be illustrated by the following elementary considerations.

Let us assume that space in the universe is a simple three-dimensional Euclidean space, and that the radio galaxies are scattered throughout the universe uniformly. Assume also for simplicity that all these sources emit the same amount of radio energy. Then if S_0 is the flux of radio energy received by our telescope from a source at unit distance, the flux of energy received from the same source if it were at a distance L would be S_0/L^2, as the intensity of the radio waves falls off as the inverse square of the distance from the source, as in the case of light or sound. Any source which is closer than a distance L will give a stronger signal, any further away than L will give a weaker signal. Now the sources closer to us than a distance L will number $4\pi/3\ N_0L^3$ if there are N_0 of them in a unit volume, as the volume of the sphere of radius L is $4\pi/3 L^3$. So now one has two expressions, one for the energy flux from a source at distance L, that is, $S=S_0/L^2$, and one for the number of sources closer than the distance L, that is, $N=4\pi/3N_0L^3$. Eliminating L from between these two equations one has the valuable expression $N=$const. $S^{-3/2}$.

This relation can be checked by the use of the quite extensive data now available on counts of the numbers of radio galaxies with different apparent intensities. Such a check will tell us if our assumptions were justified. Fortunately the assumption that all the sources are of the same intrinsic strength does not affect the validity of the relation, but a variation in the strength only produces a scatter in the results that can be removed by averaging over a sufficiently large number of observations. However, as one might have expected, this simple relation does not fit the facts. Instead of the exponent $-3/2$, a larger value seems appropriate. Some of the discrepancy may be due to the finite resolving power of the telescopes used in the surveys of the radio sky. The use of this and similar methods to discover the distribution of matter in the universe will be referred to again in the next chapter. For the different cosmological models there are different forms of the relation between S and N. Where we assumed a Euclidean space other spaces can, be used, and one would hope that observation would be able to discriminate between the rival hypotheses by testing their predictions on the distribution of the radio sources. It is of course possible in principle to apply this number counting method to galaxies observable optically; this has been tried, but technical difficulties make it extremely uncertain in this case.

It may be worth while mentioning at this point the quasistellar radio sources which have been discovered recently, and are causing a great deal of speculation. We have only referred as yet to those radio sources which have been identified with the galaxies. There are other sources which have been identified with objects that have the appearance on a photographic plate of stars; they have, however, so many peculiar properties that they have come to be known rather as quasi-stellar radio sources, or quasars. These objects are certainly not galaxies but their output of energy is enormous. The brightest, 3C273, has an energy output about two hundred times as great as that of our entire Galaxy of 10^{11} stars. Furthermore, some of these objects have a variable luminosity. The period of this variation in brightness is of the order of a few months. Now the maximum velocity with which a disturbance can be propagated is, according to the theory of relativity, the velocity of light; and for a body to vary in brightness as a whole with a period of months it must be sufficiently small for a disturbance to pass across it in a few light-months, that is, a fraction of a light-year. These objects must therefore be of this kind of size, i.e., a quasar is about a fraction of a light-year across. Remembering that our whole Galaxy is about 25 kiloparsecs, or some 800,000 light-years, in diameter, one sees that a quasar has the extraordinary property that it produces, say, two hundred times as much energy as the Galaxy from a region some million times smaller. 3C273 radiates about as much energy as 10^{12} suns.

There is a great puzzle about the source of these vast amounts of energy. It can be shown that it cannot result from nuclear reactions analogous to those we referred to in discussing the evolution of ordinary stars. In view of this astronomers are investigating other energy sources, in particular gravitational contraction, with the gravitational potential energy being released in other forms. Unfortunately this process does not seem able to account for the apparent ages of quasars, which are of the order of 10^5 to 10^6 years. The cosmological significance of the quasars is obscure, but such remarkable behaviour, if explained, may provide the key to other problems. Already they have prompted some to cast doubt on the validity of relativity theory. Also their great distances make them of particular interest. One of them, 3C147, is indeed the most distant object yet observed, being over half way to the limit of the observable universe. How such a distance is inferred will be discussed in the next section.

The expansion of the Universe

The importance of the Doppler Effect for investigating motions has already been referred to in our comments on the determination of the spiral structure and motions in the Galaxy using the 21-centimetre radio line from neutral hydrogen. From shifts in the line one could determine motions in the line of sight between the observer and the emitting or absorbing gas cloud. This effect also operates in the optical region of the spectrum. An emitting object receding from the observer appears redder than one which is approaching the observer, all the radiations of whatever wavelength having been apparently shifted to longer wavelengths. Thus if one observes a spectral line of one colour of a well defined wavelength, one can find both the direction of motion along the line of sight and the magnitude of this motion from apparent changes in the wavelength of the line.

Now if one uses a spectroscope to spread out the light from an extragalactic nebula and examines carefully the precise wavelengths of the different spectral lines in the spectrum produced, one finds that in nearly all cases the wavelength of all lines are greater than they would be from a comparable laboratory source of light. We ask ourselves if this is due to the Doppler Effect; if so the greater number of the nebulae are receding from us. To check this we will have to consider the law of shifts in the Doppler Effect. If all the shifts in wavelength in the spectrum are due to Doppler Effect, then the ratio of the change of wavelength to the true wavelength itself should be the same for all lines, or, in mathematical terms, $\delta = d\lambda/\lambda =$ constant throughout the spectrum, where δ is the ratio we have referred to, λ is the true wavelength and $d\lambda$ is the shift in wavelength. On examining the spectra of the nebulae it is found that this condition is indeed satisfied for all lines in the visible region. Attempts have been made to find whether it is constant even for radio waves, but these have been inconclusive. One must then conclude that unless there is some mysterious mechanism operating, either in the nebulae or in the space between us and the nebulae, exactly simulating the Doppler Effect, the nebulae are indeed in motion and that most of them are moving away from us.

Not only do we know that they are in motion, but we can measure their velocities quite well. It is found that in general the brighter the nebulae the slower they are moving, and the fainter they are the faster they are moving. This suggests that the more distant ones are moving away faster than the nearer ones. We can use the distances we have previously found to see if there is any quantitative correlation between the velocities of the nebulae and their distances. This correlation was first established by Hubble, and is known as Hubble's law. It can be stated mathematically as

$$c.\mathrm{d}\lambda/\lambda=H.r$$

where c is the velocity of light, $\mathrm{d}\lambda/\lambda$ is the measurable quantity δ we have referred to, H is a constant known as Hubble's constant and r is the distance of the nebula. This relation applies more or less to all the distant nebulae. It is quite remarkable that the relation between the velocities of recession and distance is so simple. It means that the further the nebula is away from us the faster it is receding from us, and the relation between its speed and its distance is linear. A nebula twice as far away as another is receding from us twice as fast.

The interpretation of these facts is quite startling. The universe is expanding. It is not expanding away from us alone because we are not necessarily at the centre of the expansion but, as will be seen after a little thought, it is expanding for any observer at any point in the universe. A group of particles expanding from one another appear to any observer within the group to be expanding away from him. And the more distant particles appear to be going away faster than the nearer ones. As the nebulae contain the bulk of the matter in the universe, one sees that the matter of the universe as a whole is expanding.

It was this discovery that set off most of our modern speculations on cosmology. However, such an expansion was predicted theoretically before it was observationally discovered. But there is a little more we require to know about the expansion before we can distinguish between some cosmological theories. Has the expansion always been going on at its present rate? Is it at present accelerating or decelerating? These questions are very difficult to answer observationally, but must be answered to get a complete picture of the expansion.

Nothing has yet been said about the actual velocities that one finds for the recession of the nebulae. These are found to be enormous, so enormous that it is most convenient to express them in terms of the universal maximum velocity, the velocity of light, which is about 3×10^{10} centimetres per second. For the quasar 3C147, the velocity of recession is over half the velocity of light. This is the largest velocity ever measured and from it one can conclude that the object is the most distant ever observed. For one can use the relation between red-shift and distance, once it has been found, to determine distances from red-shifts for objects too far away for the usual criteria of distance determination.

What, one might ask, would happen to objects twice as far away as 3C147? By the application of the Hubble formula one can deduce that their velocities would be greater than the velocity of light, which is impossible. We have thus arrived at the concept of the "edge" of the universe. Assume a body travelling at the highest possible velocity which is the velocity of light. From the Hubble formula its distance would be about 3,000 megaparsecs. Such an object would be the furthest detectable object. One concludes that it is about 3,000 megaparsecs to the edge of the observable universe. Such a deduction should not be taken too seriously. It assumes the validity of the Hubble relation far beyond the region in which it has been tested, and further assumes that space is Euclidean. But it leads to an interesting reflection. A body at the "edge" would be receding so fast that light from it would never reach us. A body slightly nearer would be observable, but the light from it would have taken so long to reach us that we would be observing it in the very distant past. A closer object would seem in the more recent past. So by observing at different distances we are observing at different times. There is thus an obvious use of the term "light-year". One observes an object at a distance of one light-year with light that left it one year ago; thus one sees it as it was one year ago. An object distant one million light-years is seen one million years in the past. So that if there are progressive evolutionary changes in the universe there may be some chance of seeing them by comparing distant, i.e., older, objects with nearer, i.e., younger, objects. If, for example, one finds that the more distant galaxies are on average nearer to one another than galaxies close at hand, this suggests that the universe was more congested in the past. This is the kind of problem that radio astronomical number counts may be able to help with.

The red-shift of the light from the nebulae is the most important piece of evidence in the development of cosmology. It is a datum that must be explained, or explained away, in any theory that is to fit the facts. And as its existence has only been known for about thirty years, it is not surprising that cosmology as a science is not much older.

CHAPTER II

COSMOLOGICAL
THEORIES

Cosmology is a physical science and like other physical sciences it presents its laws in mathematical form. Unfortunately for anyone seeking a simple understanding the mathematical methods of cosmology are particularly complicated. This is because most cosmological theories lean heavily on the General Theory of Relativity and this is notoriously recondite. There are quite simple reasons why relativity should figure so largely in cosmology. It was pointed out in the last chapter that there appear to be objects in the universe that have velocities that are sizable fractions of the velocity of light. Such objects can only be correctly described within the framework of relativity; the classical description of objects in uniform relative motion is found to be valid only when their relative velocities are small compared with the velocity of light. Furthermore, cosmology needs a law of gravitation, and it appears that in cosmological situations the appropriate one is the relativistic one and not the simpler classical Newtonian law.

It is important to distinguish between the Special and the General Theories of Relativity. In the Special Theory the effects of large relative velocities on the kinematics of bodies are taken into account, but the effects of gravitational fields are ignored. In the General Theory the effects of gravitation are included. The General Theory is that employed in most cosmological theories, a notable exception being Milne's theory of Kinematic Relativity. Now while the Special Theory of Relativity is very firmly established and is an essential part of modern physics, the General Theory is much less certain, mainly because it is so difficult to predict effects following from the theory that can be tested. In the early days of the development of the theory three empirical tests of predictions from the theory were suggested, and these still form today the main evidence of its correctness, as against the Newtonian theory of mechanics and gravitation. Two of the predicted effects, the motion of the perihelion of the planet Mercury, and the precise law of the bending of light rays in a gravitational field have been satisfactorily checked. The status of the third prediction, that of the increase of wavelength of electromagnetic radiation when produced in a region of high gravitational potential, is more doubtful. There is some difficulty in testing this prediction astronomically and the evidence is inconclusive. One must conclude that although General Relativity is an improvement on Newtonian laws and contains them as a special case it rests on comparatively little evidence. This should be borne in mind when considering its use in cosmology.

A general point to be mentioned which is true of all cosmological theories is that they treat highly simplified models of the universe and the matter in it. This is of course a feature common to many physical theories, and the normal development of a theory is from a highly simplified model by stages of increasing complexity to a sophisticated and realistic model. The simplifying assumptions are dropped one by one to give a theory of greater generality. But cosmology is still in its early days and its models are extremely simplified. One cannot, for example, consider the material in the universe as aggregated in galaxies. It is necessary to assume a universe of a uniform gas or fluid with none of the discontinuities or structural complications that occur in the actual universe. It should not be thought that therefore the models are of little value. They can lead to predictions which can be compared with the real behaviour of the universe; but it is always necessary to consider such large volumes of space that the assumption of a continuous distribution of matter is not hopelessly invalid. Cosmology cannot therefore at the present tell us anything about the behaviour of matter on a scale as small as the scale of the Galaxy. It is concerned only with the largest volumes. As the assumption of homogeneity is inapplicable to volumes with dimensions less than about 400 megaparsecs, cosmology will be concerned entirely with larger volumes.

The reason that cosmologists work with such simplified models is that only such models are amenable to mathematical analysis. If one considered the actual detailed structure of the universe it would be impossible mathematically even to make a start on the problem. It is not only in the ignoring of this detailed structure that simplifications are introduced. It is necessary to make further assumptions, the most important of which is the scientific equivalent of the statement that we see no reason why we should have a privileged position in the universe. There seems no reason why our particular view of the universe should be any different from that of observers at any other position in the universe, apart from merely local irregularities that are negligible on a cosmic scale. This is a statement of the so-called Cosmological Principle that the universe presents the same overall appearance and has the same overall properties from whatever position it is observed; it may be looked on as a simplifying postulate, or it may be considered to have a more fundamental significance.

THE EVOLUTIONARY THEORIES

The model of the universe that was derived by Einstein in 1917 has been mentioned already. It may be said to be the first true cosmological model in as much as it purported to give a physical account of the large scale properties of the whole universe. Using the General Theory of Relativity he showed that if one introduced a constant into the so-called field equations of this theory one could find a solution of these equations which described a universe whose matter was spread throughout it with a uniform density and with no random movements, and in which space had a spherical curvature, so that the universe, although unbounded, was finite. The notion of a curved space is a difficult one, but one has a two-dimensional analogy of a space which is finite and yet has no "edge" in the surface of a ball. Distances between points on the ball are finite yet there is no boundary to the surface. If the actual universe has a space which is curved, the curvature must be small enough for its effects to be negligible over the distances we usually consider, and for which a Euclidean, or flat, space has proved adequate. In the Einstein universe this curvature is determined by the amount of matter in the universe, which thus also determines the radius. If the amount of matter in the universe were to increase, the universe as a whole would shrink. This is because the gravitational properties of matter determine the character of the space in which the matter is situated.

The Einstein universe is static in the sense that it is unchanging and the matter in it is not in motion. As we have

seen, the red-shifts show that the universe is not static. But
General Relativity is also compatible with changing
models. De Sitter devised another model in which the space
has its own structure and in which matter is only introduced in order to test the properties of the model. Matter
placed in such a universe immediately expands. The
De Sitter universe, although less realistic than the Einstein
universe because of its absence of matter, showed that
there was a possibility of using relativity to predict evolutionary models in which the distribution of matter would
vary continuously.

The problem for cosmologists was then to derive a
model universe which contained matter with the observed
density and which expanded as observation showed the
extragalactic nebulae to be expanding. A model which
appeared to do this was developed by Eddington and
Lemaître. Eddington, in an investigation of the Einstein
universe, found that although the model was possible it was
unstable. A slight disturbance of the model causing it to
expand would result in a general expansion, a small contraction would lead to a general contraction. The Eddington–Lemaître model is based on this instability. The
universe is supposed to have originally been in a static
state represented by the Einstein model; this state could
have existed for an arbitrarily long time. Then some disturbance occurred which led to an expansion which
gradually accelerated to give an approximation to the
motions in the universe we observe today.

As will have been seen from the above the General
Theory of Relativity can be used to give quite different
models. It is quite compatible with the two extremes of
the Einstein and the De Sitter universes and with a large
class of other models. Indeed this is one of the embarrass-
ments of the theory and the evolutionary cosmologies that

go with it, that there are so many possible models. The only way of choosing between them is by comparison of their predictions with observation, and as yet it has not been possible to narrow down the number of models far. But the plausible relativistic models all have this in common that they represent a universe which is expanding and which was different in the past from what it is today. These are the evolutionary models, and they are the models in which progressive changes have been occurring since the present expansion began.

In these models the radius of the universe has been increasing continuously since some point in the past, but the different theories predict different rates, and differ also on whether the expansion is accelerating or decelerating. If it is decelerating then there may come a point when the expansion will be reversed and a contraction will set in; thus one would have an oscillating universe. But it is of interest to see what the evolutionary theories have to say about the distant past when the expansion began. Although mathematically they can be extrapolated backwards to an epoch when all the matter in the universe was concentrated in a point, this does not make physical sense. One can, however, assume in these theories that there was a primeval state when the density of matter was very much higher than it is now.

There has been a great deal of speculation about this dense state. As the theories enable one to conclude from the present rate of expansion of the universe to the date of the initial state it is possible to find the time at which the expansion began. Indeed one can see immediately that a very simple interpretation of the Hubble formula, assuming space is Euclidean and that the velocity of expansion has always had its present value, will give one the time of the initial state. A probable value of this time-scale of expansion is, in one of the more plausible evolutionary theories, about 13×10^9 years. As to what was happening at this time in the past one can only sketch some of the answers that have been offered.

Gamow considers that the matter compressed into a small volume would have been at a very high temperature in the form of a hot nuclear gas. Such a gas would evolve extremely rapidly. As the gas expanded according to an evolutionary model, it cooled and the protons, neutrons and electrons forming it were able to aggregate into the elements which we have today. The entire process of element-building took place very swiftly, in less than an hour. The agreement between the results of this theory and the observed abundances of the elements is quite fair. Obviously this theory is in competition with that described in the previous chapter in which the elements are considered to be built up exclusively from hydrogen in stars, and in which element-building is still continuing. In the Gamow theory the heavy elements were all produced in the very early stages of the expansion of the universe. It is possible that the two theories may be complementary, but it is too early to say. But we can be much more confident about what is happening in the interiors of stars at the present moment than we are of what happened in the hypothetical unique nuclear explosion that took place at the beginning of the expansion of the universe.

Another description of the initial state is Lemaître's hypothesis of the primeval "atom". In this picture the expansion started from a cool nucleus consisting of a nuclear fluid; such a nucleus would have many of the properties of atomic nuclei but would be much larger. Expansion set in with the fragmentation of this "atom" into smaller "atoms", in diameter a few kilometres, containing about as much matter as an ordinary star. The heavy elements are supposed to have been formed in the early stages of the breakup of these bodies, but detailed calculations are difficult, and much more work needs to be done to see if this theory can correctly predict the present abundances of the elements. Both this and Gamow's theory thus combine the notion of expanding from a dense state with a theory of the origin of the elements.

Now if such a dense, structureless initial state occurred in which all matter was reduced to a nuclear fluid, and there were no chemical elements as we know them, it is clearly impossible to say what happened before the initial point of the expansion. All traces of a previous state would have been erased by the high pressures and temperatures. So if, for example, the universe is oscillating, expanding from a point and then contracting to a point, it will have a series of "ages" in which it will be impossible for an observer living in one age to say what happened in preceding ages. The dense state puts up a block to scientific investigation of all that went before.

How would one expect the galaxies to have been formed in an evolutionary universe? After the initial explosive phase of the expansion the distribution of both radiation and matter would have been uniform. In the early stages most of the substance of the universe would indeed have been in the form of radiation, and this would control the distribution of matter. With the expansion the temperature dropped and radiation would have played a less and less important role. At some point in this development it became possible for the uniformly distributed gas and dust to condense into galaxies, or rather into the large clouds which then condensed into galaxies. Now it is thought that the fact that galaxies have all roughly the same size argues in favour of their all having been formed at about the same time. This time would have been when the universe would have been much denser than now so that the present galaxies were effectively touching, and the density of the universe was the density at present found in galaxies. This time can be found to be some 10^7 years after the beginning of the expansion. Since then the galaxies have been steadily moving away from one another and evolving into their present form.

Many attempts have been made observationally to check these evolutionary models. Consider what one might expect to find from a counting of the number of extragalactic radio sources at different distances. We mentioned that a uniform distribution of these sources would give a result of the form $N = $ const. $S^{-3/2}$ (cf. p. 59). But in an evolutionary universe one would not expect to find a uniform distribution. As one looks at the more distant sources one is looking backwards to a point in time when the universe was denser than at the present, and one would then expect the galaxies to be more closely packed than those in our neighbourhood. So an evolutionary universe should show an increasing number of radio galaxies per unit volume of space as one observes at increasing distances. An attempt to find whether this is the case was made by Ryle some years ago. It was found that this increase in density does in fact occur. But it is difficult to interpret this as a support for the theory, as it might be the case that the distant and younger galaxies are more likely to be radio emitters than the nearer and older ones.

One would also expect galaxies to show the effects of their great age, and one would not expect to observe any young galaxies near at hand, all of them being supposed to have been formed at the same epoch. It is difficult to know whether this is the case at the present time. But it is interesting in some ways to consider not so much the tests of the evolutionary theories themselves, but those tests that attempt to distinguish between their predictions and the predictions of their strongest rival, the steady-state theory.

THE STEADY-STATE THEORY

The steady-state theory of the universe has aroused a great deal of both technical and popular interest because it introduced into cosmology some extremely original and, at first sight, paradoxical ideas. Whereas in the evolutionary theories nothing was said explicitly about creation, although some illegitimately identified creation with the moment of the beginning of the expansion, the steady-state theory demanded that creation be going on continuously at the present time and in a manner susceptible to scientific investigation.

There are two different approaches to the theory. The first is due to Hoyle, the second to Bondi and Gold. Although their results are essentially the same they begin from quite different starting-points. Hoyle's approach is logically similar to that used in many of the evolutionary theories. He starts by a modification of the field equations of General Relativity to give a solution representing a universe which although expanding is of constant density. The space of the model is that used in the De Sitter universe, but to maintain the constant density of matter it is necessary to assume that matter is continually appearing to fill the gaps left by the expansion of the universe. This continuous creation of matter is thought to have been going on for all time; the reason that it has not resulted in a universe of infinite density is that the expansion of the universe pushes matter away over the observable limits of the universe.

Bondi and Gold base their form of the theory on the Perfect Cosmological Principle, that the predictions of the theory must be the same for all times and for all observers wherever situated. If the theory is to be in harmony with this principle, and if it is accepted that the universe is expanding, some form of creation of matter must occur, as if a continuous change in density occurred the universe would not appear the same to observers at different times. It is not therefore legitimate to extrapolate back the recession of the nebulae to an initial state of high density. If one were to reverse their motion and travel back in time, one would see that as they contracted backwards to a point they would gradually vanish, so that the total density of matter remained the same.

There is a price one must pay with a theory of this type, and it is the price of rejecting the Principle of Conservation of Energy and Mass, a physical law universally assumed to be true in every other branch of physical theory. But the steady-state theory does not imply that the creation of matter which it demands on a cosmic scale would affect the validity of the Principle on a terrestrial scale. The rate of creation of matter is determined by the rate of expansion of the universe, and calculations show that to keep the density of matter constant it would be necessary for only one hydrogen atom to be created in a volume of a few cubic kilometres per year. Such a minute change in the local quantity of matter would be quite undetectable in any laboratory experiment, and one's assumption of the Principle of Conservation of Energy and Mass would be unaffected in ordinary physics. Whether it is worth rejecting the Principle can only be determined by the success of the steady-state theory in accounting for the properties of the universe.

What are the observable effects of the steady-state theory and the hypothesis of continuous creation? There are at least two radio astronomical tests of the different predictions of the steady-state and the evolutionary theories, one of which we have already mentioned, the variations in the counts of the number of radio galaxies at different distances. While the evolutionary theories predict that there should be more galaxies per unit volume at greater distances, the steady-state theory predicts that conditions in distant parts of the universe must be the same as in nearby parts, so that one expects the number-density of galaxies to be constant with distance. Present observations seem to show that there is an increase in the number of galaxies per unit volume as one goes to greater distances. Ryle thinks that his observations are incompatible with the steady-state theory in its initial form, but he is unable to pinpoint which of the evolutionary models seems best, as one does not know how the probability of a galaxy becoming a radio galaxy varies with age. But a modification of the steady-state theory would seem to be able to fit his results, although at the cost of introducing an *ad hoc* hypothesis.

Another radio astronomical observation of interest is the determination of the variation of the angular diameter of the radio sources with their distance. The way in which this variation should occur can be derived for the different models, and should prove a good test between them, but at present the observations are not sufficiently refined to do this.

On the steady-state theory one expects the galaxies to be of all ages. Some will have formed recently from recently created matter, while some will be the relics of the distant past. On the evolutionary theory all galaxies should be of approximately the same age. So on looking at distant galaxies on the evolutionary theory one sees always younger galaxies, while in the steady-state theory one should see a mixture of old and young galaxies similar to the mixture we observe locally. It is not yet possible to distinguish between these two possibilities. If in the future astronomers should come to the conclusion that all galaxies observed at a given distance are of the same age, or if there should be a systematic trend in age, this would be an argument against the steady-state theory.

The present position among cosmologists is that it is extremely difficult with the observations available now to make a definite choice between the rival theories. But an important point in favour of the steady-state theory must be mentioned. This theory assumes that the universe has always had the same properties and is in effect ageless. In the evolutionary models there is a discontinuity in the initial dense state at some time in the past, say, about 10^{10} years ago. Thus such objects as stars or galaxies cannot in these models be older than 10^{10} years. Unfortunately, as we said in the previous chapter, there appear to be stars in our Galaxy which may be as old as 2×10^{10} years. There are two possible ways out of this dilemma for the evolutionist. The time-scale of the present expansion may still be in doubt by a factor of two, and the theory of dating stars by the use of stellar models is undoubtedly uncertain by at least this amount. At present more confidence is usually expressed in the former, but the stellar dating methods are unlikely to be so radically at fault for one to have much hope of their substantial error. Of course, the steady-state theory does not suffer from these time-scale difficulties. For this theory the universe has been in existence for an indefinitely long period of time, and one would expect objects of all possible ages to exist, from those formed in the most distant past to the youngest of all objects, the hydrogen atoms created at this instant.

Perhaps the greatest achievement of the steady-state theory has been not so much in developing a theory of the universe that will stand the test of time, although this is still possible, but in stimulating a theory of the origin of the elements in stars. As in this theory matter is created in its simplest possible form, that is, in the form of hydrogen atoms, some way had to be devised to transmute this hydrogen to the heavy elements continuously. Conditions had to be found in ordinary astronomical objects that would be found in all parts of the universe, under which this transmutation would be able to take place. This led to a search for such objects, and to considerable refinements in the theory of the formation of elements by nuclear processes in stars so that it is now possible to give a rough explanation of the origin of the elements without recourse to the extreme conditions of the dense initial state of the evolutionary theories. This led in turn to a deepening of our knowledge of stellar evolution and to a refinement of the methods of dating stars and stellar systems. Such a by-product of the theory of continuous creation is of the greatest value. Although the evolutionary theories have themselves inspired work on the origin of the elements and on the formation of galaxies, the results of this work have been comparatively unimportant.

A further reason for its importance in the development of cosmology is that its predictions are so definite, and so the theory is more easily capable of being disproved than its rivals. The evolutionist is at liberty to select whichever one of the evolutionary models happens to fit the observations best, and there are adjustable parameters which can improve the fit to the observational data. The steady-state model is, however, unique. Of course, this vulnerability of the theory means that it will probably in fact be disproved. The general trend of the evidence appears to be going against it. But it has certainly been a most valuable contributor to the science of cosmology; in particular, it has combated the view that cosmology is merely a branch of General Relativity.

Another argument advanced in favour of the theory was that it at last brought the concept of creation into a scientific context where it could be handled scientifically and would lose its air of mystery. This is mistaken, as we hope to show in the following chapter.

THE COSMOLOGY OF EDDINGTON

It was mentioned in the Introduction that one would expect it to be a final aim of physical science to produce a theory which would unify the theories of matter on the largest scale (cosmology), and the theories of matter on the smallest scale (quantum mechanics, atomic physics). This has not yet proved possible, but there are some quite remarkable relations between phenomena at the two extremes that are very suggestive of a link between the two realms of macro- and micro-physics and which have prompted some interesting speculations. Both Dirac and Jordan have constructed cosmologies based on such a link, but perhaps the most interesting attempt in this direction is due to Eddington.

If one collects together the fundamental constants of physics and combines them in certain ways it is found that there are a set of remarkable coincidences between the numerical values of some of the combinations. For example, the ratio of a quantity known as the radius of the universe and another quantity known as the classical radius of the electron is about 10^{39}, a pure number. The ratio of the magnitude of the force between an electron and a proton due to the electrostatic interaction between them and the magnitude of the force due to the gravitational interaction between them is also about 10^{39}; while the "number of particles in the universe" is about $(10^{39})^2$. Is one to regard these coincidences as chance, or do they express the fundamental interrelatedness of the different types of force and the properties of atoms and universes?

Eddington's cosmology is of interest not only because it attempts to answer these questions, but because of the theory of physical knowledge on which it is based He believed that the laws of physics are not inductive generalizations, but are in some sense direct consequences of our methods of measurement. This strongly a-prioristic view is well illustrated by the following significant passage from one of his works on relativity: "An intelligence, unacquainted with our universe, but acquainted with the system of thought by which the human mind interprets to itself the content of its sensory experience, should be able to attain all the knowledge of physics that we have attained by experiment. He would not deduce the particular events and objects of our experience, but he would deduce the generalizations we have based on them. For example, he would infer the existence and properties of radium, but not the dimensions of the earth." So the laws of physics should in principle be deducible from an accurate study of our methods of measurement, which are for him the methods through which the universe is not merely interpreted, but through which the laws of its structure are actually determined to be what they are. The laws of nature are thus a product of our thought-processes, and a study of these processes should lead us to physical laws quite independently of any empirical investigations. This is clearly a very radical and very ambitious position. Eddington's attempt to derive the laws of physics from a study of the processes of measurement was an intellectual *tour de force* involving the development of a new branch of mathematics. The theory is of extreme complexity and few are sufficiently well-equipped to pass judgment on its merits. It is of interest, however, to sketch the general results of his work; but it must be pointed out that these results have not found much favour among cosmologists, not only because of a suspicion of his principles and methods, but also because his conclusions do not appear to fit the facts.

Eddington began with a finite universe containing a finite number of fundamental particles. By using results from quantum mechanics he deduced that the actual number of these particles is of the order of 10^{79}. He then derived *a priori* relations between this number and other physical constants by means of which the constants could be calculated. Thus from his determination of the number of particles in the universe he claimed to derive such constants of microphysics as Planck's constant and the fine structure constant. Whitrow's comments sum up the modern reaction to this remarkable claim. "When we come to examine the core of Eddington's theory, the exact determination of N (the number of particles in the universe), we find he had no truly rigorous method of constructing it. Moreover, in recent years many new elementary sub-atomic particles have been discovered by experimental physicists for which there is no place in Eddington's theory. Instead then of regarding Eddington as the architect of a completed theory, he should be saluted as a pioneer whose ideas present a profound challenge to the imagination and point to a possible unification of hitherto disconnected concepts."

As to Eddington's neo-Kantian philosophy of science, it must be remarked that this too has found little support. While it appears to give an unsatisfactory account of the processes of scientific discovery, one must not forget the remarkable stimulus it gave to his own profound, though inconclusive, work on cosmology. Although the numerical coincidences mentioned call for an explanation, it is doubtful if Eddington's is the right one. Nevertheless, his work highlights what is obviously a very important and exciting problem, that is, the problem of the relation between atoms and the universe.

THE THEORY OF MILNE

A theory in many ways as remarkable as that of Eddington is the theory of Kinematical Relativity due to Milne. Unfortunately this theory has suffered much the same fate as Eddington's, but it has the similar merit of having subjected basic ideas in cosmology to a radical examination. It is also strongly *a priori*, and instead of following the usual practice of extending the application of local laws to the universe, it starts from cosmology and attempts to derive the normal laws of physics. If successful this would be an extraordinary achievement, but some of the conclusions of the theory were so paradoxical that it has dropped from the attention of most cosmologists.

Milne developed this theory in the 1930s when the general expansion of the universe had been shown observationally. Milne regarded this expansion as basic. He did not use the General Theory of Relativity but used only the Special Theory in a particular form which he called Kinematical Relativity. This had the advantage of avoiding the curved spaces of General Relativity and the complex mathematical apparatus that goes with it. Milne also introduced a precise definition of distance based on signalling with light rays; by measuring the passage of time needed for a light ray to reach an object and be reflected back, and using the conventional velocity of light, one can find the distance of the object. Milne used this procedure rigorously throughout his theory. It led him to the concept of different time-scales for different phenomena; atomic clocks (spectral lines) keep time on the t-scale, while dynamical clocks keep time on the τ-scale. These scales are not identical. Milne found that his uniformly expanding cosmological model described on the τ-scale could be regarded as a static model on the t-scale, and while finite in time on the τ-scale was indefinitely old on the t-scale.

Milne's actual model is identical with one of the evolutionary models of General Relativity, but arrived at in quite a different way. His deduction of the laws of physics from his cosmology has been subjected to much the same sort of criticism as Eddington's; that it is not rigorous but assumes much that has to be proved. But this extremely complex and difficult theory is again a remarkable *tour de force* if nothing else.

CREATION AND
COSMOLOGY

We have seen in the preceding chapter that the concept of creation enters cosmology in two ways. In the context of the evolutionary cosmologies the concept of creation *in the beginning* has been introduced, while in the context of the steady-state theories one first hears of *continuous* creation throughout the life span, whether finite or infinite, of the universe. It should be stressed that it is not in all types of evolutionary cosmology that an event occurs which can be described, properly or improperly, as the initial act of creation, and further that only a few workers in this field have attempted to link a feature in some of these theories with such an act of creation. But the fact remains that such an identification has sometimes been made, and that this identification is one of the reasons why so much popular attention has been given to these theories.

It is clearly of importance to determine in what sense the term creation is being used in cosmology; whether it is being used in the same sense in both types of theory as a creation *ex nihilo*; and whether on the basis of the observed facts and the methodology of the sciences the use of the term is of any philosophical or theological relevance. It is convenient to treat the two cosmological uses of the term separately, so in what follows we will first consider critically the arguments that have been offered to show that the universe is finite in time, and then the arguments for the occurrence of a continuous process of creation of matter, before commenting on the relevance of these speculations to the philosophical and theological concepts of creation and conservation. Our conclusions will not be in any way derogatory to either cosmology or theology. It is our thesis that only a series of regrettable confusions have led to friction between scientist, philosopher and theologian in the field of cosmology.

Such frictions that develop from time to time between philosophy and the natural sciences are not always due to shortcomings in the scientists; but while one must acknowledge the immense success of scientists in their understanding and mastery of the material world, one must also add that this success cannot save some of their number from the strictures of philosophers and logicians. This must not be taken to imply that philosophy and the sciences are entirely different activities which happen to share some topics as the common subject of their different disciplines; and that if the conclusions of philosopher and scientist differ those of the philosopher must take precedence. Neither does it imply that it is the business of philosophers to maintain a watching brief over the sciences, prompting acceptance of one theory and rejection of another. Rather it implies that an excessive preoccupation with the methods and habits of thought of the sciences can induce an indifference to other, perhaps more important, aspects of reality that are the particular concern of the philosopher, and that in pathological cases of this indifference the philosopher may well intervene to save the scientist from himself. An example of this indifference may be found in the well-known controversy about the implications of the axioms of Quantum Mechanics. While these axioms and their accompanying mathematical formalism make an admirable instrument for the predicting of facts and the ordering of experimental knowledge, the current interpretation of them as implying a fundamental indeterminism in the microscopic world is, at the very least, open to doubt on philosophical grounds. For the scientist immersed in the methods of empirical investigation it is, however, a quite natural interpretation while he remains within his own terms of reference. Furthermore it is one which will be accepted all the more readily if he is himself wedded to that particular philosophical theory that has made the experimental method the method appropriate to all investigations, even those not usually considered scientific.

CREATION IN THE BEGINNING AND COSMOLOGY

It is indicative of the attitude of mind characterized above that the problem of determining the age of the universe, and thus dating an initial creation, has sometimes been considered to be a problem to which the scientist could hope to offer a solution. We hope to show that a scientific solution of the problem is impossible, and to indicate the true relevance of the arguments and observations that have been used to find the time-scale of the universe.

While the difficulties that arise in attempts to determine the age of any particular object or system in the universe may be technically insurmountable with the methods of dating available today, few would doubt that advances in technique will remove these difficulties. One can reasonably expect to find in the future methods more general than those in present use, which will offer much higher degrees of accuracy. Certainly, no one doubts the possibility of dating the earth or the solar system or certain stars, and one may be reasonably confident that the estimates we now have of their ages are reliable, at least as orders of magnitude. Dating the universe as a whole, however, is obviously a completely different matter. If it is a problem to which the methods of the sciences are appropriate, it is not immediately obvious what kind of observations are going to be relevant; and finding the time-scale that includes all other time-scales is clearly going to call for some presuppositions of an epistemological nature.

There have been three approaches to answering the key question, "What is the age of the universe?". While some accept the question as both meaningful and in practice answerable, others consider that although meaningful it cannot in the present state of the evidence be answered, while others insist that *any* attempt to answer the question is in principle impossible.

The first approach is particularly simple, but has only been adopted by a few, and by those at a time when the relative ages of the earth and the time-scale of the recession of the nebulae appeared to be compatible in an evolutionary scheme. To appreciate the problems that arise from an intercomparison of the various age estimates for astronomical objects, it will be helpful to summarize the methods and results of the most important investigations, some of which have already been mentioned in Chapter I. These are arranged in order of increasing age, and also, as will be obvious, in order of increasing uncertainty.

(a) *The age of the earth*

There are a variety of radioactive methods available for determining the age of the earth's crust. It is now possible to date its formation at about $4 \cdot 5 \times 10^9$ years ago.

(b) *The age of meteorites*

Another example of radioactive dating which has some bearing on the age of the solar system is the dating of meteorites. It is generally agreed today that meteorites are members of the solar system, although there is considerable difference of opinion as to their place in it and their origin. Their ages will set a lower bound to the age of the system. As the uranium and thorium concentrations in iron meteorites are about thirty times lower than in igneous rocks, they are difficult to measure, and the uncertainties in age are greater than in terrestrial estimates. Recent work finds a maximum age of about $4 \cdot 8 \times 10^9$ years for a variety of samples. It seems clear that the different methods used concur in an upper limit to meteoritic ages close to the age of the earth's crust. The cosmogonic significance of this is obscure, if indeed this agreement has any such significance. The rough agreement of these ages with an estimate of the age of the moon from the effects of tidal friction is of interest.

(c) *The ages of stars*

The methods of determining the ages of stars based on the theory of their evolution have already been referred to. It seems now highly probable that there exist stars in the Galaxy with ages in excess of 20×10^9 years. While it would be wise to consider this figure as only accurate within a factor two, it is unlikely that the method is radically at fault. More precise knowledge of the parameters of the nuclear reactions occurring in stellar interiors, and more accurate theories of stellar development will see the reliability of these stellar ages improving.

(d) The age of the heavy elements

Once again using the theory of stellar evolution one can determine the age of terrestrial uranium as at least 6×10^9 years.

(e) The age of the Galaxy from dynamical arguments

These have been discussed before. Although they are highly uncertain, they seem to agree with the other estimates at least as orders of magnitude.

(f) The time-scale of the recession of the nebulae

As has been mentioned, what appears to be the best present value for Hubble's constant is not inconsistent with certain evolutionary models of the universe for which the time-scale since the beginning of the expansion would be as long as about 13×10^9 years.

On the basis of the results given above it seems difficult to accept an evolutionary model of the universe. A situation in which a part of the universe appears to be older than the whole, i.e., in which certain stars of our Galaxy seem to be older than the present period of expansion is paradoxical. But the estimates of stellar ages were only made with some certainty as late as 1959; before that time the stars of the Galaxy were thought to be younger than 10×10^9 years, which appeared consistent with the time-scale of the present expansion. In the context of this earlier situation there were therefore those who saw a real possibility in attempts to date the beginning of the present expansion and thus perhaps to date the beginning of the universe. The answer to the question "What is the age of the universe?" was put at about 10×10^9 years by some, while others waited for more extensive and more accurate observations. Of course, these age estimates were also interpreted by others in terms of the steady-state cosmology with no evolutionary implications.

It must be stressed that before the ages of stars were considered to be as long as they now seem to be there was a remarkable and impressive consistency in the sequence of ages of different cosmologically relevant objects. Quite differing methods depending on different branches of physical theory and technique seemed to provide a plausible time-scale for the evolution of the observable universe as a whole, and for its various parts. But one must ask what exactly is the relevance of all this to actually fixing the age of the universe. It has been mentioned at the beginning of this section that there are some who consider that there is no meaning to be attached to the question, "What is the age of the universe?". It is now necessary to determine exactly what can, and what cannot, be deduced from the astronomical results we have been considering, even assuming that one of the evolutionary models describes the actual universe.

When one attempts to date the formation of the earth one is quite clear as to what one is trying to do, and to the methods one employs in doing it. It is highly improbable that the earth has always existed; if it had one would expect there to be observable effects which are not in fact observed. There are theories of the formation of the planets of the solar system which purport to explain the origin of the earth at some point in the past. There are certainly no conceptual difficulties associated with the fact that it is finite in time. Furthermore, the physical processes used to find the date of its formation are well understood. The decay of radioactive isotopes proceeds according to strict and well determined laws; the use of these kind of isotopes as clocks is commonplace, and has found wide application in the dating of even comparatively recent events, where such dating is found to agree well with results based on other criteria, such as those employed, for example, by archaeologists or palaeontologists. In short, the method is reliable and has often been checked. One can be confident as to the accuracy of our estimate for the age of the earth.

One cannot, on the other hand, be as confident as to the ages we have quoted for some of the globular cluster stars. The theory of how such stars develop is still somewhat vague, and the observational data is not all that could be desired. But in dating such a group of stars one has no doubt as to what one is attempting to do. Once again, as with the earth, one is using a series of physical theories and observations which, although now less clearly understood, lead to a result which is a reasonable measure of the true age of the objects considered. Assuming that physical processes in stellar interiors obey the same laws that they are found to obey in the laboratory (if such processes can be experimentally reproduced) one can use them as clocks to date the formation of stars from the interstellar material.

Thus in the case of the earth and of a stellar cluster one uses more or less clearly understood physical changes to date by extrapolation into the past the objects in which the changes occur. And in these two instances it is necessary not only that the object one is considering had a beginning, but also that one understands roughly the physical laws operating at the beginning and ever since. If, however, one attempts to date the universe as a whole one is sure of neither of these things. What then is the precise nature of any estimate of the age of the universe, and what methods are in fact used in attempts to find it?

The concept of the age of the universe, if this is considered as finite and measurable, only enters into scientific discussion through one or other of the evolutionary cosmologies. As the origin of the universe, presuming that it had one, is not now in any way observable, one must in these theories make use of observations of the present state of the universe, and infer from them the nature and date of its origin. We have mentioned in earlier pages the law of the recession of the extragalactic nebulae known as Hubble's law, and have said how this law could be interpreted in terms of a dense state in the past, when the material of the universe was compressed into a much smaller volume. With an explicit theory of how the universe is expanding there is the possibility of making a precise extrapolation of the present expansion into the past according to a mathematical law. Such an explicit theory might be one or other of the evolutionary world models. It is not possible to infer the past history of the motions of the nebulae merely from the observational law; the help of one of the models is necessary. Let us then assume that we find that the observations at the present time fit one of the evolutionary models best. This model will contain a relation between the radius of the particular space used in the model and the time. As has been remarked, the expansion of the material of the nebulae may be looked upon in relativity as the expansion of the space itself. Now let us assume that in our model there is a point on the time-scale in the past where the radius of the space shrinks to nothing, that is, when the matter of the universe is considered as concentrated at a point from which it has since been continually expanding. The time elapsed between this singularity in the radius and the present is called the age of the universe. What exactly happened at the point from which the expansion began is undetermined. Obviously all the matter in the universe could not have been concentrated in a mathematical point. One assumes to make physical sense of such a situation that the mathematical singularity implies only a state in which all matter was concentrated in a space minute compared with that it now occupies. But one can expect that long before such a state is reached the conditions that are assumed to prevail in the model will have broken down.

Now if the age of the universe as defined in such a way is the age of all material things, then the hypothetical dense state "in the beginning" is to be identified with a primeval act of creation *ex nihilo*. Such a conclusion, however, clearly goes beyond the evidence. As will be readily apparent there is no ground for thinking that the technical "age of the universe", which, it must be stressed, occurs in only some of the many possible theories, has any more profound meaning than that which it actually bears in the theory. Although it gives the date of an epoch which might well represent the ultimate limit of science beyond which all would be inaccessible, traces of a preceding structure having been erased by the very high temperatures and pressures associated with the dense state, it has no relevance to the actual age of the totality of material things, except perhaps to set a lower bound to the period of time for which such things have existed. To assume that one might by the use of one of these theories put a date to the original act of creation is either to overinterpret the theory, or to be guilty of an elementary blunder in the confusion of scientific and theological terminology.

Although there are few today who would go as far as this in identifying the hypothetical beginning of the expansion of the nebulae with the act of creation, and fewer who would attempt to base a Natural Theology on this identification (although somewhat surprisingly this has been done), there have been some whose approach to the problem is vitiated by similar unjustifiable assumptions. Gamow has written a book entitled *The Creation of the Universe*, in which he sets out to give answers to "fundamental questions, such as whether or not the universe had a beginning in time".[1] He has, apparently, little difficulty with the more fundamental question as to whether this problem can be solved in the way that he attempts to solve it, from the observations and theories of astronomers. Others have adopted a more cautious position with regard to the value of the observational evidence, but consider it possible that some figure may be decided on in the future as being the age of the universe. J. T. Davies, writing in a symposium on this problem published some years ago, seems to hold this view. He writes: "What existed before the creation of the universe? How was the universe created? When was the universe created? This last question can be given an answer directly from the red-shifts."[2] He qualifies this by going on to say that, more generally, "we associate the time parameter, whether finite or infinite, in our theories with the intuitive concept of 'the age of the universe'."[3] So while he does not commit himself as to the possibility of offering a value, whether finite or infinite, for the age of the universe, it is significant that this concept is considered as something understood intuitively, and that the red-shifts and recession of the nebulae are considered as possibly relevant to dating the time of creation.

It may be doubted whether the question as to the age of the universe is in fact as simple as these writers have

[1] G. Gamow, *The Creation of the Universe* (New York, 1961), p. vii.
[2] J. T. Davies, "The Age of the Universe", *British Journal for the Philosophy of Science*, 5 (1954), p. 198.
[3] Ibid., p. 202.

taken it to be, and whether it is asking for an answer that can possibly be given in the context of the sciences. Much confusion has arisen from a misuse of the term "universe". If "universe" is taken as synonymous with "the present large-scale structure and properties of the visible universe", then their arguments have an obvious relevance, but only, of course, in an evolutionary universe. The properties and structure of such a universe would be assumed fairly continuous throughout an expansion (or contraction); a dense state at the beginning of the expansion would form a discontinuity which would effectively mark off the present state of the universe from all that went before. If, on the other hand, one takes it to mean the totality of material reality, or the totality of things and events, then the question as to the age of the universe becomes a question of dating the temporally first thing or event. That cosmologists sometimes take it in this latter sense is clear from the examples given above, and from the frequency with which the word "creation" occurs in these discussions.

It is of interest to enquire whether the temporally first thing can be dated, or if it can be shown that there was no first thing and that the universe is temporally infinite. The idea that the universe is infinite in time has in the past appealed to some on philosophical grounds on account of the difficulties involved in the concept of a first thing. The Archytas Paradox concerning the impossibility of a universe of finite extension has an obvious temporal analogue. If one stands at a hypothetical limit of the universe, it seems absurd to say that one cannot stretch one's hand outwards beyond the boundary. So no matter where one is in space there must be extension to infinity. One may avoid the paradox in the spatial case by constructing a space which is finite yet unbounded and which represents the spatial properties of the actual universe. The temporal case is more obscure, and times before the "beginning" have an irresistible fascination.

It is at least open to doubt whether any present empirical investigation can help us to decide the question as to the finite or infinite past duration of the universe. Logically, our investigations may lead us to assign a lower bound to the age of the universe, so that we may say with some confidence that the universe is at least x years old, but we cannot say that the universe is not more than y years old, nor that it is exactly z years old. This is not because of the unavoidable limitation that all our data has been collected in the last few decades, or because we have no experience of the state of affairs at the "beginning". It is because there is no physical process which can be extrapolated backwards to determine the beginning of things in general. The extrapolation back of the velocities of recession of the nebulae (granting all the assumptions usually made) might date the beginning of the present recession, if the model we choose corresponds to the actual universe. No process, however, can be extrapolated back to give the information that at $t=0$ on a time-scale all things came into existence, implying that for all t less than zero nothing existed. It follows that we cannot prove that the universe is finite in time by any observational method, but only that it has probably been in existence for at least a certain length of time.

In the light of the above it is clear that claims to give the age of the universe, if by universe is meant the totality of things, that derive from scientific observations and theories are misguided. But it should be recognized that a convention has arisen that the time-scale of the recession of the nebulae is to be called the age of the universe. In this usage "universe" is taken as equivalent to "the present large-scale structure of the universe", and the truth of one of the evolutionary theories is assumed if the age is to be finite. This convention is, to say the least, misleading. It is artificial to have to say, as one must in the present state of the evidence, that parts of the universe, for example, certain stars, are older than the universe itself. And that the convention is often confused with the reality will have been seen from the opinions that have already been mentioned. It has been pointed out that in early discussions of this subject one finds frequent reference to "the age of the universe", and that in more recent studies this has been replaced largely by the term "cosmic time-scale", which implies an attempt at establishing reference points in the past, rather than fixing an absolute beginning in cosmic time, if this were possible. This trend will certainly reduce confusion; the term "age of the universe" with its theological connotations, has been a constant source of misunderstanding, and a constant temptation to the uncritical cosmologist to attempt the impossible.

CONTINUOUS CREATION

Due in part to the difficulty with the apparently incompatible time-scale of recession and the age of the Galaxy in the evolutionary theories, the steady-state theories are receiving more attention. It is only in these theories that the concept of continuous creation enters. It should be remembered that this continuous creation of matter is not postulated in a merely qualitative fashion. Definite mathematical expressions for the rate of creation of matter are derived, quite analogous to the mathematical expressions for some other physical processes. It is considered that the creation has been in progress as long as the universe has existed, and is happening now, and will continue to happen.

The theory thus claims to give a scientific description of

creation *ex nihilo*. One of the authors of the theory considers this to be among its main achievements; "The problem of creation is brought within the scope of physical enquiry and is examined in detail instead of, as in other theories, being handed over to metaphysics."[4] He goes on to assert that "to push the entire question of creation into the past is to restrict science to a discussion of what happened after creation while forbidding it to examine creation itself. This is a counsel of despair to be taken only if everything else fails."[5]

While it may be doubted whether the evolutionary theories really do "hand creation over to metaphysics", as all the models are quite compatible with there having been no creation in time at all, it is certain that the steady-state theory itself cannot avoid the metaphysical implications of creation. For continuous creation *ex nihilo* going on at the present time offers just the same metaphysical problems as any initial creation of all things; just the same questions as to the origin of the created matter must be asked, and these are not questions to which the scientist would offer an answer. The possibility of measuring the rate of such a creation is irrelevant to the more ultimate question as to its cause. It is no argument to dub the evolutionary theories "counsels of despair" because they preclude something that one considers desirable for what are essentially extra-scientific reasons. A distaste for metaphysics and a reluctance to accept the real limitations of the experimental method should not prompt one to acceptance or rejection of any scientific theory. By the test of observation the steady-state cosmology seems, in the light of the conflict of time-scales, to have as good a chance of survival in a modified form as any other. Such a test should be recog-

[4] H. Bondi, *Cosmology* (Cambridge, 1960), p. 140.
[5] Ibid., p. 152.

nized as the only criterion of its value, or of the value of its rivals.

There is an extremely acute analysis of the methodology of the steady-state theory in a chapter of M. K. Munitz's book *Space, Time and Creation*. He points out that the claim that creation is brought within the scope of physical theory is not strictly true. The supporters of the hypothesis of continuous creation, while exploring the effects of matter "given" as existing, ignore the question of the possible antecedents which cause its existence. The so-called "physics of creation" is really an investigation of matter already in existence. Furthermore, it might be claimed that one or other of the evolutionary theories outlines a "physics of creation", for in some of these there is a description of the physical state of matter "in the beginning". Munitz notes that "by spreading creation out in time and space, there is no reduction in the mystery, since multiplication of the occasions of creation as contrasted with the single unique event leaves it open to exactly the same objections as the latter".[6]

As to the claim that the mystery in creation "in the beginning" is removed by assuming creation to be going on continuously and predictably, it must be stressed that creation is not treated causally by the theorists. Matter appears *ex nihilo* and no investigation into a scientific explanation of its appearance is offered. Although one might conceivably have a detailed scientific account of the effects of this process, in the absence of a causal explanation one is at a loss to know how the idea of continuous creation can claim to be more rigorously "scientific" than other theories of, say, an initial creation. The steady-state theory

[6] M. K. Munitz, *Space, Time and Creation* (Glencoe, Illinois, 1957), p. 157.

has itself set up a barrier to scientific investigation, in the sense that the explanation of creation is still "handed over to metaphysics" as in the case of the much maligned evolutionary theories. It has set up the fact of continuous creation as an ultimate beyond which science cannot go, in precisely the same way as those who consider that an initial dense state in an evolutionary model is to be identified with a primeval act of creation. To say that matter is being created in the universe implies the scientific impossibility of explaining its appearance. Munitz is doubtful whether the term "creation" is of any value at all in a cosmological context. Having traced the development of the concept from the original notion of a human craftsman to that of a divine purposeful maker of all things, he comments:

> Scientific cosmology, of course, now not only makes no claims about the designful character of the universe; it also stops short of making any reference to the Creator or the process of his making. It is not even claimed that these are mysteries whose existence is to be believed in even though not understood. All that it would retain is the fact that matter in an elemental form is created continuously. But if the Maker, the process of making, and the purpose are gone, *what is there left to the concept of creation?*... If the *sole content* of the concept of creation is now simply that matter appears or is present, then far from this being a case of creation, it is at best, as previously suggested, a fact which invites scientific explanation.[7]

While it may be doubted whether the "appearance" of matter *ex nihilo* can be a fact which can receive scientific explanation, this passage shows the attenuated sense which the term "creation" has come to bear in some cosmological work.

[7] Ibid., p. 165.

CREATION AND CHRISTIANITY

In a lecture on the implications of modern cosmology in his book *The Relevance of Science,* von Weizsäcker relates a story of the reaction of the distinguished German physicist Nernst to the suggestion that the universe was finite in time.[8] Nernst was of the fervent opinion that the view that there might be an age of the universe was not scientific. The point of the story is that it was obvious that although Nernst had no idea *why* it was not scientific, he was absolutely sure that the universe had no beginning. Weizsäcker traces this strong yet irrational belief to an evolution of opinion in the secularization of the last century, where according to him belief in an everlasting universe took the place of belief in an immortal soul. This seems unlikely; but what is significant is that such prejudices should exist, and that there should be such strong psychological pressures for or against the finite duration of the universe. This is in some ways surprising as it is not the sort of problem that can be settled scientifically, and it is quite irrelevant to the practice of science itself. It is, indeed, of little consequence to any philosophy of life. It is certainly not the most important feature of the Christian doctrine of creation.

To determine what a Christian approach to the problem of creation is, one must expand the ideas in the Introduction on the purpose and meaning of the Old Testament accounts. Faith in creation as such is not the position of the early parts of Genesis, neither is it their primary purpose. Both the J and the P narratives are concerned with faith in salvation and election. Although they form a synthesis of faith and a detailed physical world-picture, in

[8] C. F. von Weizsäcker, *The Relevance of Science* (London, 1964), pp. 151 et seq.

which there is complete harmony between the two, such a synthesis is not their aim. It is remarkable to see in these accounts how sharply the attitude of the biblical creation story is distinguished from that of the cosmological myths of the writers' contemporaries. One has not a mystery of procreation from which the divinity is formed, or a creative struggle of mythical forces from which the earth arose, but a description of a series of actions by one being who alone possesses creative powers. The story of creation is free from any vestige of magical thinking; there is only a formal similarity with ideas from the Babylonian myths and astrology. But the cosmological conceptions of the Israelites do not seem to have been directly influenced by their religious beliefs. In a general way they shared ideas common to the rest of the ancient world; their idea of the structure of the universe was based as much upon crude observation as on mythical concepts. They were interested in the world less from a theoretical angle than with an essentially practical aim. The only element which the idea of God the creator can be said to have added to their strictly cosmological ideas was that they considered the world to be coherent and directly related to the creator's purposes. This implies that they were deeply conscious of the aspect of finality in the world; for them everything is directed to the creator's final aim, the salvation of humanity.

One must stress this unique aspect of the biblical idea of creation. The narratives of Genesis and their poetic parallel in Psalm 104, which are the only passages of really theological reflection on creation, contain mythological elements but these are clearly subordinated to what might be called the historical importance of the account. This is the description of creation as the beginning of God's plan for the chosen people, and the uppermost idea in the writer's mind is not the mere fact of creation but the purpose of creation, the covenant with the people of Israel. While the concept of creation *ex nihilo* is implicit in the early books of the Old Testament it only becomes explicit in the Second Book of the Machabees; "Consider the heaven and the earth . . . and know that God has not made them from existing things" (8. 28).

It is in Augustine that the notion of God not merely as creator in the beginning but as a continual conserver of all things is so strongly developed. This is of course clearly a biblical concept. As the initial creation is subordinate in the mind of the Israelites to God's guidance and saving of his people, so it is subordinate to the *creatio continua* or conservation of the Augustinian scheme. So the relation between God and the world is not that between a being who fashioned the world in the beginning and then left it to evolve in a way determined by physical laws and the initial conditions at creation, but that between a being who constantly governs, directs and conserves and a world which without this conservation would cease to exist. The former position is that of an eighteenth-century Deist; the latter represents the traditional Christian attitude to creation, and it is this that makes the question of the finite or infinite duration of the universe a comparatively secondary question.

But even with such an intimate relation between the creator and creation the two are clearly distinguished. As God is considered not to be in time, time is something created together with the first things at an initial creation. This initial creation therefore marks not only the beginning of creatures but also the beginning of time. Thus a universe of infinite duration is most certainly possible. God is outside time, and it is a solecism to consider an infinitely old universe as having existed as long as its creator. An age is simply not predicable of God. Hence our only source of information on a creation in time is Scripture: without this we would have no inkling as to whether or not there had been such a creation.

It will be clear from the above that the idea of a creation proceeding continuously throughout the universe during all time would be expected to be sympathetically received by the Christian. It is certainly an idea that would seem foreign to a Deist, but to a believer in Providence it would come quite naturally. Somewhat strangely the opposite has been supposed by those who thought that there was anti-Christian polemical material in the steady-state theory.

CONCLUSION

Our conclusion must be the perhaps disappointing one that cosmology and a theology of creation can have little to contribute to one another. What we draw from cosmology about a creation in time is what we have read into cosmology. One cannot say anything about an initial creation of theological interest by resort to a telescope, neither can one use astronomy to provide a revised version of Genesis (nor, for that matter, of the Apocalypse). Stephen Toulmin[1] has summed up in an amusing way this fundamental irrelevance in a remark on Hoyle's book *The Nature of the Universe*, which was based on some radio talks in which Hoyle had concluded by stating how developments in cosmology had affected his personal view of the world.

> Fred Hoyle is said to have composed the concluding, unscientific postscript to his book because he had been amazed at the comfort which the devout had been drawing from his first few talks. Now it was legitimate enough of him to argue that such listeners must have misunderstood his talks, and that his astrophysics could not properly be taken as bolstering up their faith. But he seems to have felt something more than this: that, if properly understood, his theories should have been a source of positive *dis-*

[1] S. Toulmin, in *Metaphysical Beliefs*, ed. A. C. MacIntyre (London, 1957), p. 79.

comfort to religious people. Does this not suggest that he was deceived in the same way as they? For what is puzzling is not people's taking comfort from an astronomical theory —seeing it as a prop for their faith—rather than having religious doubts aroused, and so feeling upset by it. What we *should* boggle at is the idea that either reaction is called for, and that any direct connection exists one way or the other between Hoyle's physics and the attitude that we should adopt towards the world.

Statements about the attitude we should adopt towards the world really do have no connection with physics or chemistry or astronomy. However the science of cosmology should develop in the future, a person's belief in the truth or falsity of the Genesis account of an initial creation, properly understood, will be unaffected. It is extremely unfortunate that confusions have led scientists and others to more ambitious views on the potentialities of cosmology. Cosmology has been a subject about which dogmatic statements have been made on the basis of remarkably little evidence. Some excuse must be that the subject is intrinsically of such interest that it would be more than human nature could bear to set a moratorium on speculation before there are enough facts to make the speculations of any lasting value. But it is not this uncertainty that has led to the major confusions. These were due to invalid comparisons between the tentative results of the new science and other statements from philosophy and theology with which they appeared to have something in common. Cosmological theories are sure to become more precise and better founded, but their importance to any non-scientific discipline is not likely to increase. Although one may be grateful to them for the more profound insight they give into the nature of the universe, one will base one's attitude to the universe on insights of a different character.

GLOSSARY

Creation ex nihilo: The production from no pre-existing substance of a thing which has had no previous existence anywhere or in any way, except as an idea in the mind of a creator.

Concurrence: The activity by which the creator preserves a created thing in existence.

Magnitude: The astronomical unit of stellar or galactic brightness. The apparent magnitude of a star is its measured magnitude. Absolute magnitudes are the magnitudes which stars would have at a standard distance. From a knowledge of a star's absolute magnitude can be inferred its distance by measuring its apparent magnitude.

Colour index: A precise measure of a star's colour. It is the numerical difference in a star's magnitude as measured in two different spectral regions. The larger the colour index, the redder and cooler a star is.

SELECT BIBLIOGRAPHY

1. *Popular Accounts of Cosmological Theories*

COUDERC, P., *The Expansion of the Universe*, translated by J. B. Sidgwick, London, Faber, 1952.

GAMOW, G., *The Creation of the Universe*, New York, Macmillan, 1961.

HOYLE, F., *Frontiers of Astronomy*, London, Heinemann, 1955, and New York, Harper, 1957.

JONES, G. O., ROTBLAT, J., WHITROW, G. J., *Atoms and the Universe*, London, Eyre & Spottiswoode, and New York, Scribner, 1956.

LOVELL, A. C. B., *The Individual and the Universe*, London, Oxford Univ. Press, and New York, Harper, 1959.

LYTTLETON, R. A., *The Modern Universe*, London, Hodder & Stoughton, 1956, and New York, Harper, 1957.

SCIAMA, D. W., *The Unity of the Universe*, London, Faber, and New York, Doubleday, 1959.

WHITROW, G. J., *The Structure and Evolution of the Universe*, New York, Harper, 1959.

2. *More Advanced Accounts*

BONDI, H., *Cosmology* (2nd ed.), London and New York, Cambridge University Press, 1960.

MCVITIE, G. C., *Fact and Theory in Cosmology*, London, Eyre & Spottiswoode, 1961, and New York, Macmillan, 1962.

3. *Works with chapters on Philosophical and Theological Problems of Cosmology*

MASCALL, E. L., *Christian Theology and Natural Science*, London and New York, Longmans, 1956.

MUNITZ, M. K., *Space, Time and Creation*, Glencoe, Illinois, The Free Press, 1957; *Theories of the Universe*, New York, The Free Press, 1957.

TOULMIN, S., HEPBURN, R. W., MACINTYRE, A., *Metaphysical Beliefs*, London, S.C.M. Press, and Naperville, Ill., Allenson, 1957.

WEIZSÄCKER, C. F. VON, *The Relevance of Science*, London, Collins, 1964.

WHITTAKER, E. T., *Space and Spirit*, London, Nelson, 1964.

The Twentieth Century Encyclopedia of Catholicism

The number of each volume indicates its place in the over-all series and not the order of publication.

TWENTIETH CENTURY ENCYCLOPEDIA OF CATHOLICISM

Titles are subject to change.